This

Running Journal

2022

Belongs To:

Table of Contents

~ It's Not The *Distance* You Must Overtake In *Running*, It's Yourself That You Must Conquer~

January 2022

SUNDAY	MONDAY	TUESDAY	WEDNESDAY
30	31		
2	3	4	5
9	10	11	12
16	17	18	19
23	24	25	26

In January, my running goals are

____

____

____

Do not be afraid to fall down. It is just a very short moment to endure.

THURSDAY	FRIDAY	SATURDAY
		1
6	7	8
13	14	15
20	21	22
27	28	29

HABITS TRACKER

THINGS TO TRACK					
1	☐	☐	☐	☐	☐
2	☐	☐	☐	☐	☐
3	☐	☐	☐	☐	☐
4	☐	☐	☐	☐	☐
5	☐	☐	☐	☐	☐
6	☐	☐	☐	☐	☐
7	☐	☐	☐	☐	☐
8	☐	☐	☐	☐	☐
9	☐	☐	☐	☐	☐
10	☐	☐	☐	☐	☐
11	☐	☐	☐	☐	☐
12	☐	☐	☐	☐	☐
13	☐	☐	☐	☐	☐
14	☐	☐	☐	☐	☐
15	☐	☐	☐	☐	☐
16	☐	☐	☐	☐	☐
17	☐	☐	☐	☐	☐
18	☐	☐	☐	☐	☐
19	☐	☐	☐	☐	☐
20	☐	☐	☐	☐	☐
21	☐	☐	☐	☐	☐
22	☐	☐	☐	☐	☐
23	☐	☐	☐	☐	☐
24	☐	☐	☐	☐	☐
25	☐	☐	☐	☐	☐
26	☐	☐	☐	☐	☐
27	☐	☐	☐	☐	☐
28	☐	☐	☐	☐	☐
29	☐	☐	☐	☐	☐
30	☐	☐	☐	☐	☐
31	☐	☐	☐	☐	☐

In January, my running goals are

____

____

____

February 2022

SUNDAY	MONDAY	TUESDAY	WEDNESDAY
		1	2
6	7	8	9
13	14	15	16
20	21	22	23
27	28		

In February, my running goals are

Do small roles and piece them together later. It would get bigger and bigger.

THURSDAY	FRIDAY	SATURDAY
3	4	5
10	11	12
17	18	19
24	25	26

HABITS TRACKER

THINGS TO TRACK					
1	☐	☐	☐	☐	☐
2	☐	☐	☐	☐	☐
3	☐	☐	☐	☐	☐
4	☐	☐	☐	☐	☐
5	☐	☐	☐	☐	☐
6	☐	☐	☐	☐	☐
7	☐	☐	☐	☐	☐
8	☐	☐	☐	☐	☐
9	☐	☐	☐	☐	☐
10	☐	☐	☐	☐	☐
11	☐	☐	☐	☐	☐
12	☐	☐	☐	☐	☐
13	☐	☐	☐	☐	☐
14	☐	☐	☐	☐	☐
15	☐	☐	☐	☐	☐
16	☐	☐	☐	☐	☐
17	☐	☐	☐	☐	☐
18	☐	☐	☐	☐	☐
19	☐	☐	☐	☐	☐
20	☐	☐	☐	☐	☐
21	☐	☐	☐	☐	☐
22	☐	☐	☐	☐	☐
23	☐	☐	☐	☐	☐
24	☐	☐	☐	☐	☐
25	☐	☐	☐	☐	☐
26	☐	☐	☐	☐	☐
27	☐	☐	☐	☐	☐
28	☐	☐	☐	☐	☐
29	☐	☐	☐	☐	☐
30	☐	☐	☐	☐	☐
31	☐	☐	☐	☐	☐

In February, my running goals are

____

____

____

March 2022

SUNDAY	MONDAY	TUESDAY	WEDNESDAY
		1	2
6	7	8	9
13	14	15	16
20	21	22	23
27	28	29	30

In March, my running goals are

____

____

____

Working hard would always yield satisfying results.

THURSDAY	FRIDAY	SATURDAY
3	4	5
10	11	12
17	18	19
24	25	26
31		

HABITS TRACKER

THINGS TO TRACK					
1	☐	☐	☐	☐	☐
2	☐	☐	☐	☐	☐
3	☐	☐	☐	☐	☐
4	☐	☐	☐	☐	☐
5	☐	☐	☐	☐	☐
6	☐	☐	☐	☐	☐
7	☐	☐	☐	☐	☐
8	☐	☐	☐	☐	☐
9	☐	☐	☐	☐	☐
10	☐	☐	☐	☐	☐
11	☐	☐	☐	☐	☐
12	☐	☐	☐	☐	☐
13	☐	☐	☐	☐	☐
14	☐	☐	☐	☐	☐
15	☐	☐	☐	☐	☐
16	☐	☐	☐	☐	☐
17	☐	☐	☐	☐	☐
18	☐	☐	☐	☐	☐
19	☐	☐	☐	☐	☐
20	☐	☐	☐	☐	☐
21	☐	☐	☐	☐	☐
22	☐	☐	☐	☐	☐
23	☐	☐	☐	☐	☐
24	☐	☐	☐	☐	☐
25	☐	☐	☐	☐	☐
26	☐	☐	☐	☐	☐
27	☐	☐	☐	☐	☐
28	☐	☐	☐	☐	☐
29	☐	☐	☐	☐	☐
30	☐	☐	☐	☐	☐
31	☐	☐	☐	☐	☐

In March, my running goals are

____

____

____

April 2022

SUNDAY	MONDAY	TUESDAY	WEDNESDAY
3	4	5	6
10	11	12	13
17	18	19	20
24	25	26	27

In April, my running goals are

____

____

____

You represent what you have done. So act now!

THURSDAY	FRIDAY	SATURDAY
	1	2
7	8	9
14	15	16
21	22	23
28	29	30

In April, my running goals are

____

____

____

HABITS TRACKER

THINGS TO TRACK					
1	☐	☐	☐	☐	☐
2	☐	☐	☐	☐	☐
3	☐	☐	☐	☐	☐
4	☐	☐	☐	☐	☐
5	☐	☐	☐	☐	☐
6	☐	☐	☐	☐	☐
7	☐	☐	☐	☐	☐
8	☐	☐	☐	☐	☐
9	☐	☐	☐	☐	☐
10	☐	☐	☐	☐	☐
11	☐	☐	☐	☐	☐
12	☐	☐	☐	☐	☐
13	☐	☐	☐	☐	☐
14	☐	☐	☐	☐	☐
15	☐	☐	☐	☐	☐
16	☐	☐	☐	☐	☐
17	☐	☐	☐	☐	☐
18	☐	☐	☐	☐	☐
19	☐	☐	☐	☐	☐
20	☐	☐	☐	☐	☐
21	☐	☐	☐	☐	☐
22	☐	☐	☐	☐	☐
23	☐	☐	☐	☐	☐
24	☐	☐	☐	☐	☐
25	☐	☐	☐	☐	☐
26	☐	☐	☐	☐	☐
27	☐	☐	☐	☐	☐
28	☐	☐	☐	☐	☐
29	☐	☐	☐	☐	☐
30	☐	☐	☐	☐	☐
31	☐	☐	☐	☐	☐

May 2022

SUNDAY	MONDAY	TUESDAY	WEDNESDAY
29	30	31	
1	2	3	4
8	9	10	11
15	16	17	18
22	23	24	25

In May, my running goals are

Only way to get started? Stop talking.

THURSDAY	FRIDAY	SATURDAY
5	6	7
12	13	14
19	20	21
26	27	28

HABITS TRACKER

THINGS TO TRACK					
1	☐	☐	☐	☐	☐
2	☐	☐	☐	☐	☐
3	☐	☐	☐	☐	☐
4	☐	☐	☐	☐	☐
5	☐	☐	☐	☐	☐
6	☐	☐	☐	☐	☐
7	☐	☐	☐	☐	☐
8	☐	☐	☐	☐	☐
9	☐	☐	☐	☐	☐
10	☐	☐	☐	☐	☐
11	☐	☐	☐	☐	☐
12	☐	☐	☐	☐	☐
13	☐	☐	☐	☐	☐
14	☐	☐	☐	☐	☐
15	☐	☐	☐	☐	☐
16	☐	☐	☐	☐	☐
17	☐	☐	☐	☐	☐
18	☐	☐	☐	☐	☐
19	☐	☐	☐	☐	☐
20	☐	☐	☐	☐	☐
21	☐	☐	☐	☐	☐
22	☐	☐	☐	☐	☐
23	☐	☐	☐	☐	☐
24	☐	☐	☐	☐	☐
25	☐	☐	☐	☐	☐
26	☐	☐	☐	☐	☐
27	☐	☐	☐	☐	☐
28	☐	☐	☐	☐	☐
29	☐	☐	☐	☐	☐
30	☐	☐	☐	☐	☐
31	☐	☐	☐	☐	☐

In May, my running goals are

____

____

____

June 2022

SUNDAY	MONDAY	TUESDAY	WEDNESDAY
			1
5	6	7	8
12	13	14	15
19	20	21	22
26	27	28	29

In June, my running goals are

____

____

____

Action + Work + Perseverance = Success.

THURSDAY	FRIDAY	SATURDAY
2	3	4
9	10	11
16	17	18
23	24	25
30		

HABITS TRACKER

THINGS TO TRACK					
1	☐	☐	☐	☐	☐
2	☐	☐	☐	☐	☐
3	☐	☐	☐	☐	☐
4	☐	☐	☐	☐	☐
5	☐	☐	☐	☐	☐
6	☐	☐	☐	☐	☐
7	☐	☐	☐	☐	☐
8	☐	☐	☐	☐	☐
9	☐	☐	☐	☐	☐
10	☐	☐	☐	☐	☐
11	☐	☐	☐	☐	☐
12	☐	☐	☐	☐	☐
13	☐	☐	☐	☐	☐
14	☐	☐	☐	☐	☐
15	☐	☐	☐	☐	☐
16	☐	☐	☐	☐	☐
17	☐	☐	☐	☐	☐
18	☐	☐	☐	☐	☐
19	☐	☐	☐	☐	☐
20	☐	☐	☐	☐	☐
21	☐	☐	☐	☐	☐
22	☐	☐	☐	☐	☐
23	☐	☐	☐	☐	☐
24	☐	☐	☐	☐	☐
25	☐	☐	☐	☐	☐
26	☐	☐	☐	☐	☐
27	☐	☐	☐	☐	☐
28	☐	☐	☐	☐	☐
29	☐	☐	☐	☐	☐
30	☐	☐	☐	☐	☐
31	☐	☐	☐	☐	☐

In June, my running goals are

____

____

____

July 2022

SUNDAY	MONDAY	TUESDAY	WEDNESDAY
31			
3	4	5	6
10	11	12	13
17	18	19	20
24	25	26	27

In July, my running goals are

____

____

____

If you are afraid of one thing, then that thing is probably worth it to try.

THURSDAY	FRIDAY	SATURDAY
	1	2
7	8	9
14	15	16
21	22	23
28	29	30

HABITS TRACKER

THINGS TO TRACK					
1	☐	☐	☐	☐	☐
2	☐	☐	☐	☐	☐
3	☐	☐	☐	☐	☐
4	☐	☐	☐	☐	☐
5	☐	☐	☐	☐	☐
6	☐	☐	☐	☐	☐
7	☐	☐	☐	☐	☐
8	☐	☐	☐	☐	☐
9	☐	☐	☐	☐	☐
10	☐	☐	☐	☐	☐
11	☐	☐	☐	☐	☐
12	☐	☐	☐	☐	☐
13	☐	☐	☐	☐	☐
14	☐	☐	☐	☐	☐
15	☐	☐	☐	☐	☐
16	☐	☐	☐	☐	☐
17	☐	☐	☐	☐	☐
18	☐	☐	☐	☐	☐
19	☐	☐	☐	☐	☐
20	☐	☐	☐	☐	☐
21	☐	☐	☐	☐	☐
22	☐	☐	☐	☐	☐
23	☐	☐	☐	☐	☐
24	☐	☐	☐	☐	☐
25	☐	☐	☐	☐	☐
26	☐	☐	☐	☐	☐
27	☐	☐	☐	☐	☐
28	☐	☐	☐	☐	☐
29	☐	☐	☐	☐	☐
30	☐	☐	☐	☐	☐
31	☐	☐	☐	☐	☐

In July, my running goals are

____

____

____

August 2022

SUNDAY	MONDAY	TUESDAY	WEDNESDAY
	1	2	3
7	8	9	10
14	15	16	17
21	22	23	24
28	29	30	31

In August, my running goals are

____

____

____

The best feeling comes after the most difficult climb.

THURSDAY	FRIDAY	SATURDAY
4	5	6
11	12	13
18	19	20
25	26	27

HABITS TRACKER

THINGS TO TRACK					
1	☐	☐	☐	☐	☐
2	☐	☐	☐	☐	☐
3	☐	☐	☐	☐	☐
4	☐	☐	☐	☐	☐
5	☐	☐	☐	☐	☐
6	☐	☐	☐	☐	☐
7	☐	☐	☐	☐	☐
8	☐	☐	☐	☐	☐
9	☐	☐	☐	☐	☐
10	☐	☐	☐	☐	☐
11	☐	☐	☐	☐	☐
12	☐	☐	☐	☐	☐
13	☐	☐	☐	☐	☐
14	☐	☐	☐	☐	☐
15	☐	☐	☐	☐	☐
16	☐	☐	☐	☐	☐
17	☐	☐	☐	☐	☐
18	☐	☐	☐	☐	☐
19	☐	☐	☐	☐	☐
20	☐	☐	☐	☐	☐
21	☐	☐	☐	☐	☐
22	☐	☐	☐	☐	☐
23	☐	☐	☐	☐	☐
24	☐	☐	☐	☐	☐
25	☐	☐	☐	☐	☐
26	☐	☐	☐	☐	☐
27	☐	☐	☐	☐	☐
28	☐	☐	☐	☐	☐
29	☐	☐	☐	☐	☐
30	☐	☐	☐	☐	☐
31	☐	☐	☐	☐	☐

In August, my running goals are

____

____

____

September 2022

SUNDAY	MONDAY	TUESDAY	WEDNESDAY
4	5	6	7
11	12	13	14
18	19	20	21
25	26	27	28

In September, my running goals are

____

____

____

Rather than live sitting down. I would rather die on an adventure.

THURSDAY	FRIDAY	SATURDAY
1	2	3
8	9	10
15	16	17
22	23	24
29	30	

In September, my running goals are

____

____

____

HABITS TRACKER

THINGS TO TRACK					
1	☐	☐	☐	☐	☐
2	☐	☐	☐	☐	☐
3	☐	☐	☐	☐	☐
4	☐	☐	☐	☐	☐
5	☐	☐	☐	☐	☐
6	☐	☐	☐	☐	☐
7	☐	☐	☐	☐	☐
8	☐	☐	☐	☐	☐
9	☐	☐	☐	☐	☐
10	☐	☐	☐	☐	☐
11	☐	☐	☐	☐	☐
12	☐	☐	☐	☐	☐
13	☐	☐	☐	☐	☐
14	☐	☐	☐	☐	☐
15	☐	☐	☐	☐	☐
16	☐	☐	☐	☐	☐
17	☐	☐	☐	☐	☐
18	☐	☐	☐	☐	☐
19	☐	☐	☐	☐	☐
20	☐	☐	☐	☐	☐
21	☐	☐	☐	☐	☐
22	☐	☐	☐	☐	☐
23	☐	☐	☐	☐	☐
24	☐	☐	☐	☐	☐
25	☐	☐	☐	☐	☐
26	☐	☐	☐	☐	☐
27	☐	☐	☐	☐	☐
28	☐	☐	☐	☐	☐
29	☐	☐	☐	☐	☐
30	☐	☐	☐	☐	☐
31	☐	☐	☐	☐	☐

2022

SUNDAY	MONDAY	TUESDAY	WEDNESDAY
30	31		
2	3	4	5
9	10	11	12
16	17	18	19
23	24	25	26

In October, my running goals are

____

____

____

Actions are the best life lessons.

THURSDAY	FRIDAY	SATURDAY
		1
6	7	8
13	14	15
20	21	22
27	28	29

HABITS TRACKER

THINGS TO TRACK					
1	☐	☐	☐	☐	☐
2	☐	☐	☐	☐	☐
3	☐	☐	☐	☐	☐
4	☐	☐	☐	☐	☐
5	☐	☐	☐	☐	☐
6	☐	☐	☐	☐	☐
7	☐	☐	☐	☐	☐
8	☐	☐	☐	☐	☐
9	☐	☐	☐	☐	☐
10	☐	☐	☐	☐	☐
11	☐	☐	☐	☐	☐
12	☐	☐	☐	☐	☐
13	☐	☐	☐	☐	☐
14	☐	☐	☐	☐	☐
15	☐	☐	☐	☐	☐
16	☐	☐	☐	☐	☐
17	☐	☐	☐	☐	☐
18	☐	☐	☐	☐	☐
19	☐	☐	☐	☐	☐
20	☐	☐	☐	☐	☐
21	☐	☐	☐	☐	☐
22	☐	☐	☐	☐	☐
23	☐	☐	☐	☐	☐
24	☐	☐	☐	☐	☐
25	☐	☐	☐	☐	☐
26	☐	☐	☐	☐	☐
27	☐	☐	☐	☐	☐
28	☐	☐	☐	☐	☐
29	☐	☐	☐	☐	☐
30	☐	☐	☐	☐	☐
31	☐	☐	☐	☐	☐

In October, my running goals are

____

____

____

November 2022

SUNDAY	MONDAY	TUESDAY	WEDNESDAY
		1	2
6	7	8	9
13	14	15	16
20	21	22	23
27	28	29	30

In November, my running goals are

____

____

____

One thing to give up before success? Excuses.

THURSDAY	FRIDAY	SATURDAY
3	4	5
10	11	12
17	18	19
24	25	26

HABITS TRACKER

THINGS TO TRACK					
1	☐	☐	☐	☐	☐
2	☐	☐	☐	☐	☐
3	☐	☐	☐	☐	☐
4	☐	☐	☐	☐	☐
5	☐	☐	☐	☐	☐
6	☐	☐	☐	☐	☐
7	☐	☐	☐	☐	☐
8	☐	☐	☐	☐	☐
9	☐	☐	☐	☐	☐
10	☐	☐	☐	☐	☐
11	☐	☐	☐	☐	☐
12	☐	☐	☐	☐	☐
13	☐	☐	☐	☐	☐
14	☐	☐	☐	☐	☐
15	☐	☐	☐	☐	☐
16	☐	☐	☐	☐	☐
17	☐	☐	☐	☐	☐
18	☐	☐	☐	☐	☐
19	☐	☐	☐	☐	☐
20	☐	☐	☐	☐	☐
21	☐	☐	☐	☐	☐
22	☐	☐	☐	☐	☐
23	☐	☐	☐	☐	☐
24	☐	☐	☐	☐	☐
25	☐	☐	☐	☐	☐
26	☐	☐	☐	☐	☐
27	☐	☐	☐	☐	☐
28	☐	☐	☐	☐	☐
29	☐	☐	☐	☐	☐
30	☐	☐	☐	☐	☐
31	☐	☐	☐	☐	☐

In November, my running goals are

____

____

____

December 2022

SUNDAY	MONDAY	TUESDAY	WEDNESDAY
4	5	6	7
11	12	13	14
18	19	20	21
25	26	27	28

In December, my running goals are

____

____

____

THURSDAY	FRIDAY	SATURDAY
1	2	3
8	9	10
15	16	17
22	23	24
29	30	31

HABITS TRACKER

THINGS TO TRACK					
1	☐	☐	☐	☐	☐
2	☐	☐	☐	☐	☐
3	☐	☐	☐	☐	☐
4	☐	☐	☐	☐	☐
5	☐	☐	☐	☐	☐
6	☐	☐	☐	☐	☐
7	☐	☐	☐	☐	☐
8	☐	☐	☐	☐	☐
9	☐	☐	☐	☐	☐
10	☐	☐	☐	☐	☐
11	☐	☐	☐	☐	☐
12	☐	☐	☐	☐	☐
13	☐	☐	☐	☐	☐
14	☐	☐	☐	☐	☐
15	☐	☐	☐	☐	☐
16	☐	☐	☐	☐	☐
17	☐	☐	☐	☐	☐
18	☐	☐	☐	☐	☐
19	☐	☐	☐	☐	☐
20	☐	☐	☐	☐	☐
21	☐	☐	☐	☐	☐
22	☐	☐	☐	☐	☐
23	☐	☐	☐	☐	☐
24	☐	☐	☐	☐	☐
25	☐	☐	☐	☐	☐
26	☐	☐	☐	☐	☐
27	☐	☐	☐	☐	☐
28	☐	☐	☐	☐	☐
29	☐	☐	☐	☐	☐
30	☐	☐	☐	☐	☐
31	☐	☐	☐	☐	☐

In December, my running goals are

____

____

____

December

Week 1 ~ 12/27/2021 to 1/2/2022

Dec 27. MON

Hours Slept: | Sleep Quality: 1 2 3 4 5 | Morning HR: | Hyration: | Warm Up:
Time Of Day: | Pace: | Distance: | Weather: | Aches/Pains/Injury:
Route:

Dec 28. TUE

Hours Slept: | Sleep Quality: 1 2 3 4 5 | Morning HR: | Hyration: | Warm Up:
Time Of Day: | Pace: | Distance: | Weather: | Aches/Pains/Injury:
Route:

Dec 29. WED

Hours Slept: | Sleep Quality: 1 2 3 4 5 | Morning HR: | Hyration: | Warm Up:
Time Of Day: | Pace: | Distance: | Weather: | Aches/Pains/Injury:
Route:

Dec 30. THU

Hours Slept: | Sleep Quality: 1 2 3 4 5 | Morning HR: | Hyration: | Warm Up:
Time Of Day: | Pace: | Distance: | Weather: | Aches/Pains/Injury:
Route:

Dec 31. FRI

Hours Slept: | Sleep Quality: 1 2 3 4 5 | Morning HR: | Hyration: | Warm Up:
Time Of Day: | Pace: | Distance: | Weather: | Aches/Pains/Injury:
Route:

Jan 1. SAT

Hours Slept: | Sleep Quality: 1 2 3 4 5 | Morning HR: | Hyration: | Warm Up:
Time Of Day: | Pace: | Distance: | Weather: | Aches/Pains/Injury:
Route:

Jan 2. SUN

Hours Slept: | Sleep Quality: 1 2 3 4 5 | Morning HR: | Hyration: | Warm Up:
Time Of Day: | Pace: | Distance: | Weather: | Aches/Pains/Injury:
Route:

January

Week 2 ~ 1/3/2022 to 1/9/2022

Jan 3. MON

Hours Slept: | Sleep Quality: 1 2 3 4 5 | Morning HR: | Hyration: | Warm Up:

Time Of Day: | Pace: | Distance: | Weather: | Aches/Pains/Injury:

Route:

Jan 4. TUE

Hours Slept: | Sleep Quality: 1 2 3 4 5 | Morning HR: | Hyration: | Warm Up:

Time Of Day: | Pace: | Distance: | Weather: | Aches/Pains/Injury:

Route:

Jan 5. WED

Hours Slept: | Sleep Quality: 1 2 3 4 5 | Morning HR: | Hyration: | Warm Up:

Time Of Day: | Pace: | Distance: | Weather: | Aches/Pains/Injury:

Route:

Jan 6. THU

Hours Slept: | Sleep Quality: 1 2 3 4 5 | Morning HR: | Hyration: | Warm Up:

Time Of Day: | Pace: | Distance: | Weather: | Aches/Pains/Injury:

Route:

Jan 7. FRI

Hours Slept: | Sleep Quality: 1 2 3 4 5 | Morning HR: | Hyration: | Warm Up:

Time Of Day: | Pace: | Distance: | Weather: | Aches/Pains/Injury:

Route:

Jan 8. SAT

Hours Slept: | Sleep Quality: 1 2 3 4 5 | Morning HR: | Hyration: | Warm Up:

Time Of Day: | Pace: | Distance: | Weather: | Aches/Pains/Injury:

Route:

Jan 9. SUN

Hours Slept: | Sleep Quality: 1 2 3 4 5 | Morning HR: | Hyration: | Warm Up:

Time Of Day: | Pace: | Distance: | Weather: | Aches/Pains/Injury:

Route:

January

Week 3 ~ 1/10/2022 to 1/16/2022

Jan 10. MON

Hours Slept: Sleep Quality: 1 2 3 4 5 Morning HR: Hyration: Warm Up:
Time Of Day: Pace: Distance: Weather: Aches/Pains/Injury:
Route:

Jan 11. TUE

Hours Slept: Sleep Quality: 1 2 3 4 5 Morning HR: Hyration: Warm Up:
Time Of Day: Pace: Distance: Weather: Aches/Pains/Injury:
Route:

Jan 12. WED

Hours Slept: Sleep Quality: 1 2 3 4 5 Morning HR: Hyration: Warm Up:
Time Of Day: Pace: Distance: Weather: Aches/Pains/Injury:
Route:

Jan 13. THU

Hours Slept: Sleep Quality: 1 2 3 4 5 Morning HR: Hyration: Warm Up:
Time Of Day: Pace: Distance: Weather: Aches/Pains/Injury:
Route:

Jan 14. FRI

Hours Slept: Sleep Quality: 1 2 3 4 5 Morning HR: Hyration: Warm Up:
Time Of Day: Pace: Distance: Weather: Aches/Pains/Injury:
Route:

Jan 15. SAT

Hours Slept: Sleep Quality: 1 2 3 4 5 Morning HR: Hyration: Warm Up:
Time Of Day: Pace: Distance: Weather: Aches/Pains/Injury:
Route:

Jan 16. SUN

Hours Slept: Sleep Quality: 1 2 3 4 5 Morning HR: Hyration: Warm Up:
Time Of Day: Pace: Distance: Weather: Aches/Pains/Injury:
Route:

January

Week 4 ~ 1/17/2022 to 1/23/2022

Jan 17. MON
Hours Slept: Sleep Quality: 1 2 3 4 5 Morning HR: Hyration: Warm Up:
Time Of Day: Pace: Distance: Weather: Aches/Pains/Injury:
Route:

Jan 18. TUE
Hours Slept: Sleep Quality: 1 2 3 4 5 Morning HR: Hyration: Warm Up:
Time Of Day: Pace: Distance: Weather: Aches/Pains/Injury:
Route:

Jan 19. WED
Hours Slept: Sleep Quality: 1 2 3 4 5 Morning HR: Hyration: Warm Up:
Time Of Day: Pace: Distance: Weather: Aches/Pains/Injury:
Route:

Jan 20. THU
Hours Slept: Sleep Quality: 1 2 3 4 5 Morning HR: Hyration: Warm Up:
Time Of Day: Pace: Distance: Weather: Aches/Pains/Injury:
Route:

Jan 21. FRI
Hours Slept: Sleep Quality: 1 2 3 4 5 Morning HR: Hyration: Warm Up:
Time Of Day: Pace: Distance: Weather: Aches/Pains/Injury:
Route:

Jan 22. SAT
Hours Slept: Sleep Quality: 1 2 3 4 5 Morning HR: Hyration: Warm Up:
Time Of Day: Pace: Distance: Weather: Aches/Pains/Injury:
Route:

Jan 23. SUN
Hours Slept: Sleep Quality: 1 2 3 4 5 Morning HR: Hyration: Warm Up:
Time Of Day: Pace: Distance: Weather: Aches/Pains/Injury:
Route:

January

Week 5 ~ 1/24/2022 to 1/30/2022

Jan 24. MON

Hours Slept: | Sleep Quality: 1 2 3 4 5 | Morning HR: | Hyration: | Warm Up:
Time Of Day: | Pace: | Distance: | Weather: | Aches/Pains/Injury:
Route:

Jan 25. TUE

Hours Slept: | Sleep Quality: 1 2 3 4 5 | Morning HR: | Hyration: | Warm Up:
Time Of Day: | Pace: | Distance: | Weather: | Aches/Pains/Injury:
Route:

Jan 26. WED

Hours Slept: | Sleep Quality: 1 2 3 4 5 | Morning HR: | Hyration: | Warm Up:
Time Of Day: | Pace: | Distance: | Weather: | Aches/Pains/Injury:
Route:

Jan 27. THU

Hours Slept: | Sleep Quality: 1 2 3 4 5 | Morning HR: | Hyration: | Warm Up:
Time Of Day: | Pace: | Distance: | Weather: | Aches/Pains/Injury:
Route:

Jan 28. FRI

Hours Slept: | Sleep Quality: 1 2 3 4 5 | Morning HR: | Hyration: | Warm Up:
Time Of Day: | Pace: | Distance: | Weather: | Aches/Pains/Injury:
Route:

Jan 29. SAT

Hours Slept: | Sleep Quality: 1 2 3 4 5 | Morning HR: | Hyration: | Warm Up:
Time Of Day: | Pace: | Distance: | Weather: | Aches/Pains/Injury:
Route:

Jan 30. SUN

Hours Slept: | Sleep Quality: 1 2 3 4 5 | Morning HR: | Hyration: | Warm Up:
Time Of Day: | Pace: | Distance: | Weather: | Aches/Pains/Injury:
Route:

January

Week 6 ~ 1/31/2022 to 2/6/2022

Jan 31. MON

Hours Slept: | Sleep Quality: 1 2 3 4 5 | Morning HR: | Hyration: | Warm Up:
Time Of Day: | Pace: | Distance: | Weather: | Aches/Pains/Injury:
Route:

Feb 1. TUE

Hours Slept: | Sleep Quality: 1 2 3 4 5 | Morning HR: | Hyration: | Warm Up:
Time Of Day: | Pace: | Distance: | Weather: | Aches/Pains/Injury:
Route:

Feb 2. WED

Hours Slept: | Sleep Quality: 1 2 3 4 5 | Morning HR: | Hyration: | Warm Up:
Time Of Day: | Pace: | Distance: | Weather: | Aches/Pains/Injury:
Route:

Feb 3. THU

Hours Slept: | Sleep Quality: 1 2 3 4 5 | Morning HR: | Hyration: | Warm Up:
Time Of Day: | Pace: | Distance: | Weather: | Aches/Pains/Injury:
Route:

Feb 4. FRI

Hours Slept: | Sleep Quality: 1 2 3 4 5 | Morning HR: | Hyration: | Warm Up:
Time Of Day: | Pace: | Distance: | Weather: | Aches/Pains/Injury:
Route:

Feb 5. SAT

Hours Slept: | Sleep Quality: 1 2 3 4 5 | Morning HR: | Hyration: | Warm Up:
Time Of Day: | Pace: | Distance: | Weather: | Aches/Pains/Injury:
Route:

Feb 6. SUN

Hours Slept: | Sleep Quality: 1 2 3 4 5 | Morning HR: | Hyration: | Warm Up:
Time Of Day: | Pace: | Distance: | Weather: | Aches/Pains/Injury:
Route:

February

Week 7 ~ 2/7/2022 to 2/13/2022

Feb 7. MON

Hours Slept: | Sleep Quality: 1 2 3 4 5 | Morning HR: | Hyration: | Warm Up:
Time Of Day: | Pace: | Distance: | Weather: | Aches/Pains/Injury:
Route:

Feb 8. TUE

Hours Slept: | Sleep Quality: 1 2 3 4 5 | Morning HR: | Hyration: | Warm Up:
Time Of Day: | Pace: | Distance: | Weather: | Aches/Pains/Injury:
Route:

Feb 9. WED

Hours Slept: | Sleep Quality: 1 2 3 4 5 | Morning HR: | Hyration: | Warm Up:
Time Of Day: | Pace: | Distance: | Weather: | Aches/Pains/Injury:
Route:

Feb 10. THU

Hours Slept: | Sleep Quality: 1 2 3 4 5 | Morning HR: | Hyration: | Warm Up:
Time Of Day: | Pace: | Distance: | Weather: | Aches/Pains/Injury:
Route:

Feb 11. FRI

Hours Slept: | Sleep Quality: 1 2 3 4 5 | Morning HR: | Hyration: | Warm Up:
Time Of Day: | Pace: | Distance: | Weather: | Aches/Pains/Injury:
Route:

Feb 12. SAT

Hours Slept: | Sleep Quality: 1 2 3 4 5 | Morning HR: | Hyration: | Warm Up:
Time Of Day: | Pace: | Distance: | Weather: | Aches/Pains/Injury:
Route:

Feb 13. SUN

Hours Slept: | Sleep Quality: 1 2 3 4 5 | Morning HR: | Hyration: | Warm Up:
Time Of Day: | Pace: | Distance: | Weather: | Aches/Pains/Injury:
Route:

February

Week 8 ~ 2/14/2022 to 2/20/2022

Feb 14. MON

Hours Slept: | Sleep Quality: 1 2 3 4 5 | Morning HR: | Hyration: | Warm Up:

Time Of Day: | Pace: | Distance: | Weather: | Aches/Pains/Injury:

Route:

Feb 15. TUE

Hours Slept: | Sleep Quality: 1 2 3 4 5 | Morning HR: | Hyration: | Warm Up:

Time Of Day: | Pace: | Distance: | Weather: | Aches/Pains/Injury:

Route:

Feb 16. WED

Hours Slept: | Sleep Quality: 1 2 3 4 5 | Morning HR: | Hyration: | Warm Up:

Time Of Day: | Pace: | Distance: | Weather: | Aches/Pains/Injury:

Route:

Feb 17. THU

Hours Slept: | Sleep Quality: 1 2 3 4 5 | Morning HR: | Hyration: | Warm Up:

Time Of Day: | Pace: | Distance: | Weather: | Aches/Pains/Injury:

Route:

Feb 18. FRI

Hours Slept: | Sleep Quality: 1 2 3 4 5 | Morning HR: | Hyration: | Warm Up:

Time Of Day: | Pace: | Distance: | Weather: | Aches/Pains/Injury:

Route:

Feb 19. SAT

Hours Slept: | Sleep Quality: 1 2 3 4 5 | Morning HR: | Hyration: | Warm Up:

Time Of Day: | Pace: | Distance: | Weather: | Aches/Pains/Injury:

Route:

Feb 20. SUN

Hours Slept: | Sleep Quality: 1 2 3 4 5 | Morning HR: | Hyration: | Warm Up:

Time Of Day: | Pace: | Distance: | Weather: | Aches/Pains/Injury:

Route:

February

Week 9 ~ 2/21/2022 to 2/27/2022

Feb 21. MON

Hours Slept: | Sleep Quality: 1 2 3 4 5 | Morning HR: | Hyration: | Warm Up:
Time Of Day: | Pace: | Distance: | Weather: | Aches/Pains/Injury:
Route:

Feb 22. TUE

Hours Slept: | Sleep Quality: 1 2 3 4 5 | Morning HR: | Hyration: | Warm Up:
Time Of Day: | Pace: | Distance: | Weather: | Aches/Pains/Injury:
Route:

Feb 23. WED

Hours Slept: | Sleep Quality: 1 2 3 4 5 | Morning HR: | Hyration: | Warm Up:
Time Of Day: | Pace: | Distance: | Weather: | Aches/Pains/Injury:
Route:

Feb 24. THU

Hours Slept: | Sleep Quality: 1 2 3 4 5 | Morning HR: | Hyration: | Warm Up:
Time Of Day: | Pace: | Distance: | Weather: | Aches/Pains/Injury:
Route:

Feb 25. FRI

Hours Slept: | Sleep Quality: 1 2 3 4 5 | Morning HR: | Hyration: | Warm Up:
Time Of Day: | Pace: | Distance: | Weather: | Aches/Pains/Injury:
Route:

Feb 26. SAT

Hours Slept: | Sleep Quality: 1 2 3 4 5 | Morning HR: | Hyration: | Warm Up:
Time Of Day: | Pace: | Distance: | Weather: | Aches/Pains/Injury:
Route:

Feb 27. SUN

Hours Slept: | Sleep Quality: 1 2 3 4 5 | Morning HR: | Hyration: | Warm Up:
Time Of Day: | Pace: | Distance: | Weather: | Aches/Pains/Injury:
Route:

February

Week 10 ~ 2/28/2022 to 3/6/2022

Feb 28. MON

Hours Slept: | Sleep Quality: 1 2 3 4 5 | Morning HR: | Hyration: | Warm Up:
Time Of Day: | Pace: | Distance: | Weather: | Aches/Pains/Injury:
Route:

Mar 1. TUE

Hours Slept: | Sleep Quality: 1 2 3 4 5 | Morning HR: | Hyration: | Warm Up:
Time Of Day: | Pace: | Distance: | Weather: | Aches/Pains/Injury:
Route:

Mar 2. WED

Hours Slept: | Sleep Quality: 1 2 3 4 5 | Morning HR: | Hyration: | Warm Up:
Time Of Day: | Pace: | Distance: | Weather: | Aches/Pains/Injury:
Route:

Mar 3. THU

Hours Slept: | Sleep Quality: 1 2 3 4 5 | Morning HR: | Hyration: | Warm Up:
Time Of Day: | Pace: | Distance: | Weather: | Aches/Pains/Injury:
Route:

Mar 4. FRI

Hours Slept: | Sleep Quality: 1 2 3 4 5 | Morning HR: | Hyration: | Warm Up:
Time Of Day: | Pace: | Distance: | Weather: | Aches/Pains/Injury:
Route:

Mar 5. SAT

Hours Slept: | Sleep Quality: 1 2 3 4 5 | Morning HR: | Hyration: | Warm Up:
Time Of Day: | Pace: | Distance: | Weather: | Aches/Pains/Injury:
Route:

Mar 6. SUN

Hours Slept: | Sleep Quality: 1 2 3 4 5 | Morning HR: | Hyration: | Warm Up:
Time Of Day: | Pace: | Distance: | Weather: | Aches/Pains/Injury:
Route:

March

Week 11 ~ 3/7/2022 to 3/13/2022

Mar 7. MON

Hours Slept: | Sleep Quality: 1 2 3 4 5 | Morning HR: | Hyration: | Warm Up:
Time Of Day: | Pace: | Distance: | Weather: | Aches/Pains/Injury:
Route:

Mar 8. TUE

Hours Slept: | Sleep Quality: 1 2 3 4 5 | Morning HR: | Hyration: | Warm Up:
Time Of Day: | Pace: | Distance: | Weather: | Aches/Pains/Injury:
Route:

Mar 9. WED

Hours Slept: | Sleep Quality: 1 2 3 4 5 | Morning HR: | Hyration: | Warm Up:
Time Of Day: | Pace: | Distance: | Weather: | Aches/Pains/Injury:
Route:

Mar 10. THU

Hours Slept: | Sleep Quality: 1 2 3 4 5 | Morning HR: | Hyration: | Warm Up:
Time Of Day: | Pace: | Distance: | Weather: | Aches/Pains/Injury:
Route:

Mar 11. FRI

Hours Slept: | Sleep Quality: 1 2 3 4 5 | Morning HR: | Hyration: | Warm Up:
Time Of Day: | Pace: | Distance: | Weather: | Aches/Pains/Injury:
Route:

Mar 12. SAT

Hours Slept: | Sleep Quality: 1 2 3 4 5 | Morning HR: | Hyration: | Warm Up:
Time Of Day: | Pace: | Distance: | Weather: | Aches/Pains/Injury:
Route:

Mar 13. SUN

Hours Slept: | Sleep Quality: 1 2 3 4 5 | Morning HR: | Hyration: | Warm Up:
Time Of Day: | Pace: | Distance: | Weather: | Aches/Pains/Injury:
Route:

March

Week 12 ~ 3/14/2022 to 3/20/2022

Mar 14. MON

Hours Slept: | Sleep Quality: 1 2 3 4 5 | Morning HR: | Hyration: | Warm Up:
Time Of Day: | Pace: | Distance: | Weather: | Aches/Pains/Injury:
Route:

Mar 15. TUE

Hours Slept: | Sleep Quality: 1 2 3 4 5 | Morning HR: | Hyration: | Warm Up:
Time Of Day: | Pace: | Distance: | Weather: | Aches/Pains/Injury:
Route:

Mar 16. WED

Hours Slept: | Sleep Quality: 1 2 3 4 5 | Morning HR: | Hyration: | Warm Up:
Time Of Day: | Pace: | Distance: | Weather: | Aches/Pains/Injury:
Route:

Mar 17. THU

Hours Slept: | Sleep Quality: 1 2 3 4 5 | Morning HR: | Hyration: | Warm Up:
Time Of Day: | Pace: | Distance: | Weather: | Aches/Pains/Injury:
Route:

Mar 18. FRI

Hours Slept: | Sleep Quality: 1 2 3 4 5 | Morning HR: | Hyration: | Warm Up:
Time Of Day: | Pace: | Distance: | Weather: | Aches/Pains/Injury:
Route:

Mar 19. SAT

Hours Slept: | Sleep Quality: 1 2 3 4 5 | Morning HR: | Hyration: | Warm Up:
Time Of Day: | Pace: | Distance: | Weather: | Aches/Pains/Injury:
Route:

Mar 20. SUN

Hours Slept: | Sleep Quality: 1 2 3 4 5 | Morning HR: | Hyration: | Warm Up:
Time Of Day: | Pace: | Distance: | Weather: | Aches/Pains/Injury:
Route:

March

Week 13 ~ 3/21/2022 to 3/27/2022

Mar 21. MON

Hours Slept: | Sleep Quality: 1 2 3 4 5 | Morning HR: | Hyration: | Warm Up:

Time Of Day: | Pace: | Distance: | Weather: | Aches/Pains/Injury:

Route:

Mar 22. TUE

Hours Slept: | Sleep Quality: 1 2 3 4 5 | Morning HR: | Hyration: | Warm Up:

Time Of Day: | Pace: | Distance: | Weather: | Aches/Pains/Injury:

Route:

Mar 23. WED

Hours Slept: | Sleep Quality: 1 2 3 4 5 | Morning HR: | Hyration: | Warm Up:

Time Of Day: | Pace: | Distance: | Weather: | Aches/Pains/Injury:

Route:

Mar 24. THU

Hours Slept: | Sleep Quality: 1 2 3 4 5 | Morning HR: | Hyration: | Warm Up:

Time Of Day: | Pace: | Distance: | Weather: | Aches/Pains/Injury:

Route:

Mar 25. FRI

Hours Slept: | Sleep Quality: 1 2 3 4 5 | Morning HR: | Hyration: | Warm Up:

Time Of Day: | Pace: | Distance: | Weather: | Aches/Pains/Injury:

Route:

Mar 26. SAT

Hours Slept: | Sleep Quality: 1 2 3 4 5 | Morning HR: | Hyration: | Warm Up:

Time Of Day: | Pace: | Distance: | Weather: | Aches/Pains/Injury:

Route:

Mar 27. SUN

Hours Slept: | Sleep Quality: 1 2 3 4 5 | Morning HR: | Hyration: | Warm Up:

Time Of Day: | Pace: | Distance: | Weather: | Aches/Pains/Injury:

Route:

March

Week 14 ~ 3/28/2022 to 4/3/2022

Mar 28. MON	Hours Slept:	Sleep Quality: 1 2 3 4 5	Morning HR:	Hyration:	Warm Up:
	Time Of Day:	Pace:	Distance:	Weather:	Aches/Pains/Injury:
	Route:				
Mar 29. TUE	Hours Slept:	Sleep Quality: 1 2 3 4 5	Morning HR:	Hyration:	Warm Up:
	Time Of Day:	Pace:	Distance:	Weather:	Aches/Pains/Injury:
	Route:				
Mar 30. WED	Hours Slept:	Sleep Quality: 1 2 3 4 5	Morning HR:	Hyration:	Warm Up:
	Time Of Day:	Pace:	Distance:	Weather:	Aches/Pains/Injury:
	Route:				
Mar 31. THU	Hours Slept:	Sleep Quality: 1 2 3 4 5	Morning HR:	Hyration:	Warm Up:
	Time Of Day:	Pace:	Distance:	Weather:	Aches/Pains/Injury:
	Route:				
Apr 1. FRI	Hours Slept:	Sleep Quality: 1 2 3 4 5	Morning HR:	Hyration:	Warm Up:
	Time Of Day:	Pace:	Distance:	Weather:	Aches/Pains/Injury:
	Route:				
Apr 2. SAT	Hours Slept:	Sleep Quality: 1 2 3 4 5	Morning HR:	Hyration:	Warm Up:
	Time Of Day:	Pace:	Distance:	Weather:	Aches/Pains/Injury:
	Route:				
Apr 3. SUN	Hours Slept:	Sleep Quality: 1 2 3 4 5	Morning HR:	Hyration:	Warm Up:
	Time Of Day:	Pace:	Distance:	Weather:	Aches/Pains/Injury:
	Route:				

April

Week 15 ~ 4/4/2022 to 4/10/2022

Apr 4. MON

Hours Slept: | Sleep Quality: 1 2 3 4 5 | Morning HR: | Hyration: | Warm Up:
Time Of Day: | Pace: | Distance: | Weather: | Aches/Pains/Injury:
Route:

Apr 5. TUE

Hours Slept: | Sleep Quality: 1 2 3 4 5 | Morning HR: | Hyration: | Warm Up:
Time Of Day: | Pace: | Distance: | Weather: | Aches/Pains/Injury:
Route:

Apr 6. WED

Hours Slept: | Sleep Quality: 1 2 3 4 5 | Morning HR: | Hyration: | Warm Up:
Time Of Day: | Pace: | Distance: | Weather: | Aches/Pains/Injury:
Route:

Apr 7. THU

Hours Slept: | Sleep Quality: 1 2 3 4 5 | Morning HR: | Hyration: | Warm Up:
Time Of Day: | Pace: | Distance: | Weather: | Aches/Pains/Injury:
Route:

Apr 8. FRI

Hours Slept: | Sleep Quality: 1 2 3 4 5 | Morning HR: | Hyration: | Warm Up:
Time Of Day: | Pace: | Distance: | Weather: | Aches/Pains/Injury:
Route:

Apr 9. SAT

Hours Slept: | Sleep Quality: 1 2 3 4 5 | Morning HR: | Hyration: | Warm Up:
Time Of Day: | Pace: | Distance: | Weather: | Aches/Pains/Injury:
Route:

Apr 10. SUN

Hours Slept: | Sleep Quality: 1 2 3 4 5 | Morning HR: | Hyration: | Warm Up:
Time Of Day: | Pace: | Distance: | Weather: | Aches/Pains/Injury:
Route:

April

Week 16 ~ 4/11/2022 to 4/17/2022

Apr 11. MON

Hours Slept: Sleep Quality: 1 2 3 4 5 Morning HR: Hyration: Warm Up:
Time Of Day: Pace: Distance: Weather: Aches/Pains/Injury:
Route:

Apr 12. TUE

Hours Slept: Sleep Quality: 1 2 3 4 5 Morning HR: Hyration: Warm Up:
Time Of Day: Pace: Distance: Weather: Aches/Pains/Injury:
Route:

Apr 13. WED

Hours Slept: Sleep Quality: 1 2 3 4 5 Morning HR: Hyration: Warm Up:
Time Of Day: Pace: Distance: Weather: Aches/Pains/Injury:
Route:

Apr 14. THU

Hours Slept: Sleep Quality: 1 2 3 4 5 Morning HR: Hyration: Warm Up:
Time Of Day: Pace: Distance: Weather: Aches/Pains/Injury:
Route:

Apr 15. FRI

Hours Slept: Sleep Quality: 1 2 3 4 5 Morning HR: Hyration: Warm Up:
Time Of Day: Pace: Distance: Weather: Aches/Pains/Injury:
Route:

Apr 16. SAT

Hours Slept: Sleep Quality: 1 2 3 4 5 Morning HR: Hyration: Warm Up:
Time Of Day: Pace: Distance: Weather: Aches/Pains/Injury:
Route:

Apr 17. SUN

Hours Slept: Sleep Quality: 1 2 3 4 5 Morning HR: Hyration: Warm Up:
Time Of Day: Pace: Distance: Weather: Aches/Pains/Injury:
Route:

April

Week 17 ~ 4/18/2022 to 4/24/2022

Apr 18. MON

Hours Slept: | Sleep Quality: 1 2 3 4 5 | Morning HR: | Hyration: | Warm Up:

Time Of Day: | Pace: | Distance: | Weather: | Aches/Pains/Injury:

Route:

Apr 19. TUE

Hours Slept: | Sleep Quality: 1 2 3 4 5 | Morning HR: | Hyration: | Warm Up:

Time Of Day: | Pace: | Distance: | Weather: | Aches/Pains/Injury:

Route:

Apr 20. WED

Hours Slept: | Sleep Quality: 1 2 3 4 5 | Morning HR: | Hyration: | Warm Up:

Time Of Day: | Pace: | Distance: | Weather: | Aches/Pains/Injury:

Route:

Apr 21. THU

Hours Slept: | Sleep Quality: 1 2 3 4 5 | Morning HR: | Hyration: | Warm Up:

Time Of Day: | Pace: | Distance: | Weather: | Aches/Pains/Injury:

Route:

Apr 22. FRI

Hours Slept: | Sleep Quality: 1 2 3 4 5 | Morning HR: | Hyration: | Warm Up:

Time Of Day: | Pace: | Distance: | Weather: | Aches/Pains/Injury:

Route:

Apr 23. SAT

Hours Slept: | Sleep Quality: 1 2 3 4 5 | Morning HR: | Hyration: | Warm Up:

Time Of Day: | Pace: | Distance: | Weather: | Aches/Pains/Injury:

Route:

Apr 24. SUN

Hours Slept: | Sleep Quality: 1 2 3 4 5 | Morning HR: | Hyration: | Warm Up:

Time Of Day: | Pace: | Distance: | Weather: | Aches/Pains/Injury:

Route:

April

Week 18 ~ 4/25/2022 to 5/1/2022

Apr 25. MON

Hours Slept: Sleep Quality: 1 2 3 4 5 Morning HR: Hyration: Warm Up:

Time Of Day: Pace: Distance: Weather: Aches/Pains/Injury:

Route:

Apr 26. TUE

Hours Slept: Sleep Quality: 1 2 3 4 5 Morning HR: Hyration: Warm Up:

Time Of Day: Pace: Distance: Weather: Aches/Pains/Injury:

Route:

Apr 27. WED

Hours Slept: Sleep Quality: 1 2 3 4 5 Morning HR: Hyration: Warm Up:

Time Of Day: Pace: Distance: Weather: Aches/Pains/Injury:

Route:

Apr 28. THU

Hours Slept: Sleep Quality: 1 2 3 4 5 Morning HR: Hyration: Warm Up:

Time Of Day: Pace: Distance: Weather: Aches/Pains/Injury:

Route:

Apr 29. FRI

Hours Slept: Sleep Quality: 1 2 3 4 5 Morning HR: Hyration: Warm Up:

Time Of Day: Pace: Distance: Weather: Aches/Pains/Injury:

Route:

Apr 30. SAT

Hours Slept: Sleep Quality: 1 2 3 4 5 Morning HR: Hyration: Warm Up:

Time Of Day: Pace: Distance: Weather: Aches/Pains/Injury:

Route:

May 1. SUN

Hours Slept: Sleep Quality: 1 2 3 4 5 Morning HR: Hyration: Warm Up:

Time Of Day: Pace: Distance: Weather: Aches/Pains/Injury:

Route:

May

Week 19 ~ 5/2/2022 to 5/8/2022

May 2. MON

Hours Slept: | Sleep Quality: 1 2 3 4 5 | Morning HR: | Hyration: | Warm Up:

Time Of Day: | Pace: | Distance: | Weather: | Aches/Pains/Injury:

Route:

May 3. TUE

Hours Slept: | Sleep Quality: 1 2 3 4 5 | Morning HR: | Hyration: | Warm Up:

Time Of Day: | Pace: | Distance: | Weather: | Aches/Pains/Injury:

Route:

May 4. WED

Hours Slept: | Sleep Quality: 1 2 3 4 5 | Morning HR: | Hyration: | Warm Up:

Time Of Day: | Pace: | Distance: | Weather: | Aches/Pains/Injury:

Route:

May 5. THU

Hours Slept: | Sleep Quality: 1 2 3 4 5 | Morning HR: | Hyration: | Warm Up:

Time Of Day: | Pace: | Distance: | Weather: | Aches/Pains/Injury:

Route:

May 6. FRI

Hours Slept: | Sleep Quality: 1 2 3 4 5 | Morning HR: | Hyration: | Warm Up:

Time Of Day: | Pace: | Distance: | Weather: | Aches/Pains/Injury:

Route:

May 7. SAT

Hours Slept: | Sleep Quality: 1 2 3 4 5 | Morning HR: | Hyration: | Warm Up:

Time Of Day: | Pace: | Distance: | Weather: | Aches/Pains/Injury:

Route:

May 8. SUN

Hours Slept: | Sleep Quality: 1 2 3 4 5 | Morning HR: | Hyration: | Warm Up:

Time Of Day: | Pace: | Distance: | Weather: | Aches/Pains/Injury:

Route:

May

Week 20 ~ 5/9/2022 to 5/15/2022

May 9. MON

Hours Slept: | Sleep Quality: 1 2 3 4 5 | Morning HR: | Hyration: | Warm Up:
Time Of Day: | Pace: | Distance: | Weather: | Aches/Pains/Injury:
Route:

May 10. TUE

Hours Slept: | Sleep Quality: 1 2 3 4 5 | Morning HR: | Hyration: | Warm Up:
Time Of Day: | Pace: | Distance: | Weather: | Aches/Pains/Injury:
Route:

May 11. WED

Hours Slept: | Sleep Quality: 1 2 3 4 5 | Morning HR: | Hyration: | Warm Up:
Time Of Day: | Pace: | Distance: | Weather: | Aches/Pains/Injury:
Route:

May 12. THU

Hours Slept: | Sleep Quality: 1 2 3 4 5 | Morning HR: | Hyration: | Warm Up:
Time Of Day: | Pace: | Distance: | Weather: | Aches/Pains/Injury:
Route:

May 13. FRI

Hours Slept: | Sleep Quality: 1 2 3 4 5 | Morning HR: | Hyration: | Warm Up:
Time Of Day: | Pace: | Distance: | Weather: | Aches/Pains/Injury:
Route:

May 14. SAT

Hours Slept: | Sleep Quality: 1 2 3 4 5 | Morning HR: | Hyration: | Warm Up:
Time Of Day: | Pace: | Distance: | Weather: | Aches/Pains/Injury:
Route:

May 15. SUN

Hours Slept: | Sleep Quality: 1 2 3 4 5 | Morning HR: | Hyration: | Warm Up:
Time Of Day: | Pace: | Distance: | Weather: | Aches/Pains/Injury:
Route:

May

Week 21 ~ 5/16/2022 to 5/22/2022

May 16. MON

Hours Slept: | Sleep Quality: 1 2 3 4 5 | Morning HR: | Hyration: | Warm Up:
Time Of Day: | Pace: | Distance: | Weather: | Aches/Pains/Injury:
Route:

May 17. TUE

Hours Slept: | Sleep Quality: 1 2 3 4 5 | Morning HR: | Hyration: | Warm Up:
Time Of Day: | Pace: | Distance: | Weather: | Aches/Pains/Injury:
Route:

May 18. WED

Hours Slept: | Sleep Quality: 1 2 3 4 5 | Morning HR: | Hyration: | Warm Up:
Time Of Day: | Pace: | Distance: | Weather: | Aches/Pains/Injury:
Route:

May 19. THU

Hours Slept: | Sleep Quality: 1 2 3 4 5 | Morning HR: | Hyration: | Warm Up:
Time Of Day: | Pace: | Distance: | Weather: | Aches/Pains/Injury:
Route:

May 20. FRI

Hours Slept: | Sleep Quality: 1 2 3 4 5 | Morning HR: | Hyration: | Warm Up:
Time Of Day: | Pace: | Distance: | Weather: | Aches/Pains/Injury:
Route:

May 21. SAT

Hours Slept: | Sleep Quality: 1 2 3 4 5 | Morning HR: | Hyration: | Warm Up:
Time Of Day: | Pace: | Distance: | Weather: | Aches/Pains/Injury:
Route:

May 22. SUN

Hours Slept: | Sleep Quality: 1 2 3 4 5 | Morning HR: | Hyration: | Warm Up:
Time Of Day: | Pace: | Distance: | Weather: | Aches/Pains/Injury:
Route:

May

Week 22 ~ 5/23/2022 to 5/29/2022

May 23. MON

Hours Slept: | Sleep Quality: 1 2 3 4 5 | Morning HR: | Hyration: | Warm Up:
Time Of Day: | Pace: | Distance: | Weather: | Aches/Pains/Injury:
Route:

May 24. TUE

Hours Slept: | Sleep Quality: 1 2 3 4 5 | Morning HR: | Hyration: | Warm Up:
Time Of Day: | Pace: | Distance: | Weather: | Aches/Pains/Injury:
Route:

May 25. WED

Hours Slept: | Sleep Quality: 1 2 3 4 5 | Morning HR: | Hyration: | Warm Up:
Time Of Day: | Pace: | Distance: | Weather: | Aches/Pains/Injury:
Route:

May 26. THU

Hours Slept: | Sleep Quality: 1 2 3 4 5 | Morning HR: | Hyration: | Warm Up:
Time Of Day: | Pace: | Distance: | Weather: | Aches/Pains/Injury:
Route:

May 27. FRI

Hours Slept: | Sleep Quality: 1 2 3 4 5 | Morning HR: | Hyration: | Warm Up:
Time Of Day: | Pace: | Distance: | Weather: | Aches/Pains/Injury:
Route:

May 28. SAT

Hours Slept: | Sleep Quality: 1 2 3 4 5 | Morning HR: | Hyration: | Warm Up:
Time Of Day: | Pace: | Distance: | Weather: | Aches/Pains/Injury:
Route:

May 29. SUN

Hours Slept: | Sleep Quality: 1 2 3 4 5 | Morning HR: | Hyration: | Warm Up:
Time Of Day: | Pace: | Distance: | Weather: | Aches/Pains/Injury:
Route:

May

Week 23 ~ 5/30/2022 to 6/5/2022

May 30. MON

Hours Slept: | Sleep Quality: 1 2 3 4 5 | Morning HR: | Hyration: | Warm Up:
Time Of Day: | Pace: | Distance: | Weather: | Aches/Pains/Injury:
Route:

May 31. TUE

Hours Slept: | Sleep Quality: 1 2 3 4 5 | Morning HR: | Hyration: | Warm Up:
Time Of Day: | Pace: | Distance: | Weather: | Aches/Pains/Injury:
Route:

Jun 1. WED

Hours Slept: | Sleep Quality: 1 2 3 4 5 | Morning HR: | Hyration: | Warm Up:
Time Of Day: | Pace: | Distance: | Weather: | Aches/Pains/Injury:
Route:

Jun 2. THU

Hours Slept: | Sleep Quality: 1 2 3 4 5 | Morning HR: | Hyration: | Warm Up:
Time Of Day: | Pace: | Distance: | Weather: | Aches/Pains/Injury:
Route:

Jun 3. FRI

Hours Slept: | Sleep Quality: 1 2 3 4 5 | Morning HR: | Hyration: | Warm Up:
Time Of Day: | Pace: | Distance: | Weather: | Aches/Pains/Injury:
Route:

Jun 4. SAT

Hours Slept: | Sleep Quality: 1 2 3 4 5 | Morning HR: | Hyration: | Warm Up:
Time Of Day: | Pace: | Distance: | Weather: | Aches/Pains/Injury:
Route:

Jun 5. SUN

Hours Slept: | Sleep Quality: 1 2 3 4 5 | Morning HR: | Hyration: | Warm Up:
Time Of Day: | Pace: | Distance: | Weather: | Aches/Pains/Injury:
Route:

June

Week 24 ~ 6/6/2022 to 6/12/2022

Jun 6. MON

Hours Slept: Sleep Quality: 1 2 3 4 5 Morning HR: Hyration: Warm Up:
Time Of Day: Pace: Distance: Weather: Aches/Pains/Injury:
Route:

Jun 7. TUE

Hours Slept: Sleep Quality: 1 2 3 4 5 Morning HR: Hyration: Warm Up:
Time Of Day: Pace: Distance: Weather: Aches/Pains/Injury:
Route:

Jun 8. WED

Hours Slept: Sleep Quality: 1 2 3 4 5 Morning HR: Hyration: Warm Up:
Time Of Day: Pace: Distance: Weather: Aches/Pains/Injury:
Route:

Jun 9. THU

Hours Slept: Sleep Quality: 1 2 3 4 5 Morning HR: Hyration: Warm Up:
Time Of Day: Pace: Distance: Weather: Aches/Pains/Injury:
Route:

Jun 10. FRI

Hours Slept: Sleep Quality: 1 2 3 4 5 Morning HR: Hyration: Warm Up:
Time Of Day: Pace: Distance: Weather: Aches/Pains/Injury:
Route:

Jun 11. SAT

Hours Slept: Sleep Quality: 1 2 3 4 5 Morning HR: Hyration: Warm Up:
Time Of Day: Pace: Distance: Weather: Aches/Pains/Injury:
Route:

Jun 12. SUN

Hours Slept: Sleep Quality: 1 2 3 4 5 Morning HR: Hyration: Warm Up:
Time Of Day: Pace: Distance: Weather: Aches/Pains/Injury:
Route:

June

Week 25 ~ 6/13/2022 to 6/19/2022

Jun 13. MON

Hours Slept: | Sleep Quality: 1 2 3 4 5 | Morning HR: | Hyration: | Warm Up:
Time Of Day: | Pace: | Distance: | Weather: | Aches/Pains/Injury:
Route:

Jun 14. TUE

Hours Slept: | Sleep Quality: 1 2 3 4 5 | Morning HR: | Hyration: | Warm Up:
Time Of Day: | Pace: | Distance: | Weather: | Aches/Pains/Injury:
Route:

Jun 15. WED

Hours Slept: | Sleep Quality: 1 2 3 4 5 | Morning HR: | Hyration: | Warm Up:
Time Of Day: | Pace: | Distance: | Weather: | Aches/Pains/Injury:
Route:

Jun 16. THU

Hours Slept: | Sleep Quality: 1 2 3 4 5 | Morning HR: | Hyration: | Warm Up:
Time Of Day: | Pace: | Distance: | Weather: | Aches/Pains/Injury:
Route:

Jun 17. FRI

Hours Slept: | Sleep Quality: 1 2 3 4 5 | Morning HR: | Hyration: | Warm Up:
Time Of Day: | Pace: | Distance: | Weather: | Aches/Pains/Injury:
Route:

Jun 18. SAT

Hours Slept: | Sleep Quality: 1 2 3 4 5 | Morning HR: | Hyration: | Warm Up:
Time Of Day: | Pace: | Distance: | Weather: | Aches/Pains/Injury:
Route:

Jun 19. SUN

Hours Slept: | Sleep Quality: 1 2 3 4 5 | Morning HR: | Hyration: | Warm Up:
Time Of Day: | Pace: | Distance: | Weather: | Aches/Pains/Injury:
Route:

June

Week 26 ~ 6/20/2022 to 6/26/2022

Jun 20. MON

Hours Slept: Sleep Quality: 1 2 3 4 5 Morning HR: Hyration: Warm Up:

Time Of Day: Pace: Distance: Weather: Aches/Pains/Injury:

Route:

Jun 21. TUE

Hours Slept: Sleep Quality: 1 2 3 4 5 Morning HR: Hyration: Warm Up:

Time Of Day: Pace: Distance: Weather: Aches/Pains/Injury:

Route:

Jun 22. WED

Hours Slept: Sleep Quality: 1 2 3 4 5 Morning HR: Hyration: Warm Up:

Time Of Day: Pace: Distance: Weather: Aches/Pains/Injury:

Route:

Jun 23. THU

Hours Slept: Sleep Quality: 1 2 3 4 5 Morning HR: Hyration: Warm Up:

Time Of Day: Pace: Distance: Weather: Aches/Pains/Injury:

Route:

Jun 24. FRI

Hours Slept: Sleep Quality: 1 2 3 4 5 Morning HR: Hyration: Warm Up:

Time Of Day: Pace: Distance: Weather: Aches/Pains/Injury:

Route:

Jun 25. SAT

Hours Slept: Sleep Quality: 1 2 3 4 5 Morning HR: Hyration: Warm Up:

Time Of Day: Pace: Distance: Weather: Aches/Pains/Injury:

Route:

Jun 26. SUN

Hours Slept: Sleep Quality: 1 2 3 4 5 Morning HR: Hyration: Warm Up:

Time Of Day: Pace: Distance: Weather: Aches/Pains/Injury:

Route:

June

Week 27 ~ 6/27/2022 to 7/3/2022

Jun 27. MON

Hours Slept: Sleep Quality: 1 2 3 4 5 Morning HR: Hyration: Warm Up:
Time Of Day: Pace: Distance: Weather: Aches/Pains/Injury:
Route:

Jun 28. TUE

Hours Slept: Sleep Quality: 1 2 3 4 5 Morning HR: Hyration: Warm Up:
Time Of Day: Pace: Distance: Weather: Aches/Pains/Injury:
Route:

Jun 29. WED

Hours Slept: Sleep Quality: 1 2 3 4 5 Morning HR: Hyration: Warm Up:
Time Of Day: Pace: Distance: Weather: Aches/Pains/Injury:
Route:

Jun 30. THU

Hours Slept: Sleep Quality: 1 2 3 4 5 Morning HR: Hyration: Warm Up:
Time Of Day: Pace: Distance: Weather: Aches/Pains/Injury:
Route:

Jul 1. FRI

Hours Slept: Sleep Quality: 1 2 3 4 5 Morning HR: Hyration: Warm Up:
Time Of Day: Pace: Distance: Weather: Aches/Pains/Injury:
Route:

Jul 2. SAT

Hours Slept: Sleep Quality: 1 2 3 4 5 Morning HR: Hyration: Warm Up:
Time Of Day: Pace: Distance: Weather: Aches/Pains/Injury:
Route:

Jul 3. SUN

Hours Slept: Sleep Quality: 1 2 3 4 5 Morning HR: Hyration: Warm Up:
Time Of Day: Pace: Distance: Weather: Aches/Pains/Injury:
Route:

July

Week 28 ~ 7/4/2022 to 7/10/2022

Jul 4. MON

Hours Slept: | Sleep Quality: 1 2 3 4 5 | Morning HR: | Hyration: | Warm Up:
Time Of Day: | Pace: | Distance: | Weather: | Aches/Pains/Injury:
Route:

Jul 5. TUE

Hours Slept: | Sleep Quality: 1 2 3 4 5 | Morning HR: | Hyration: | Warm Up:
Time Of Day: | Pace: | Distance: | Weather: | Aches/Pains/Injury:
Route:

Jul 6. WED

Hours Slept: | Sleep Quality: 1 2 3 4 5 | Morning HR: | Hyration: | Warm Up:
Time Of Day: | Pace: | Distance: | Weather: | Aches/Pains/Injury:
Route:

Jul 7. THU

Hours Slept: | Sleep Quality: 1 2 3 4 5 | Morning HR: | Hyration: | Warm Up:
Time Of Day: | Pace: | Distance: | Weather: | Aches/Pains/Injury:
Route:

Jul 8. FRI

Hours Slept: | Sleep Quality: 1 2 3 4 5 | Morning HR: | Hyration: | Warm Up:
Time Of Day: | Pace: | Distance: | Weather: | Aches/Pains/Injury:
Route:

Jul 9. SAT

Hours Slept: | Sleep Quality: 1 2 3 4 5 | Morning HR: | Hyration: | Warm Up:
Time Of Day: | Pace: | Distance: | Weather: | Aches/Pains/Injury:
Route:

Jul 10. SUN

Hours Slept: | Sleep Quality: 1 2 3 4 5 | Morning HR: | Hyration: | Warm Up:
Time Of Day: | Pace: | Distance: | Weather: | Aches/Pains/Injury:
Route:

July

Week 29 ~ 7/11/2022 to 7/17/2022

Jul 11. MON

Hours Slept: | Sleep Quality: 1 2 3 4 5 | Morning HR: | Hyration: | Warm Up:
Time Of Day: | Pace: | Distance: | Weather: | Aches/Pains/Injury:
Route:

Jul 12. TUE

Hours Slept: | Sleep Quality: 1 2 3 4 5 | Morning HR: | Hyration: | Warm Up:
Time Of Day: | Pace: | Distance: | Weather: | Aches/Pains/Injury:
Route:

Jul 13. WED

Hours Slept: | Sleep Quality: 1 2 3 4 5 | Morning HR: | Hyration: | Warm Up:
Time Of Day: | Pace: | Distance: | Weather: | Aches/Pains/Injury:
Route:

Jul 14. THU

Hours Slept: | Sleep Quality: 1 2 3 4 5 | Morning HR: | Hyration: | Warm Up:
Time Of Day: | Pace: | Distance: | Weather: | Aches/Pains/Injury:
Route:

Jul 15. FRI

Hours Slept: | Sleep Quality: 1 2 3 4 5 | Morning HR: | Hyration: | Warm Up:
Time Of Day: | Pace: | Distance: | Weather: | Aches/Pains/Injury:
Route:

Jul 16. SAT

Hours Slept: | Sleep Quality: 1 2 3 4 5 | Morning HR: | Hyration: | Warm Up:
Time Of Day: | Pace: | Distance: | Weather: | Aches/Pains/Injury:
Route:

Jul 17. SUN

Hours Slept: | Sleep Quality: 1 2 3 4 5 | Morning HR: | Hyration: | Warm Up:
Time Of Day: | Pace: | Distance: | Weather: | Aches/Pains/Injury:
Route:

July

Week 30 ~ 7/18/2022 to 7/24/2022

Jul 18. MON

Hours Slept: | Sleep Quality: 1 2 3 4 5 | Morning HR: | Hyration: | Warm Up:
Time Of Day: | Pace: | Distance: | Weather: | Aches/Pains/Injury:
Route:

Jul 19. TUE

Hours Slept: | Sleep Quality: 1 2 3 4 5 | Morning HR: | Hyration: | Warm Up:
Time Of Day: | Pace: | Distance: | Weather: | Aches/Pains/Injury:
Route:

Jul 20. WED

Hours Slept: | Sleep Quality: 1 2 3 4 5 | Morning HR: | Hyration: | Warm Up:
Time Of Day: | Pace: | Distance: | Weather: | Aches/Pains/Injury:
Route:

Jul 21. THU

Hours Slept: | Sleep Quality: 1 2 3 4 5 | Morning HR: | Hyration: | Warm Up:
Time Of Day: | Pace: | Distance: | Weather: | Aches/Pains/Injury:
Route:

Jul 22. FRI

Hours Slept: | Sleep Quality: 1 2 3 4 5 | Morning HR: | Hyration: | Warm Up:
Time Of Day: | Pace: | Distance: | Weather: | Aches/Pains/Injury:
Route:

Jul 23. SAT

Hours Slept: | Sleep Quality: 1 2 3 4 5 | Morning HR: | Hyration: | Warm Up:
Time Of Day: | Pace: | Distance: | Weather: | Aches/Pains/Injury:
Route:

Jul 24. SUN

Hours Slept: | Sleep Quality: 1 2 3 4 5 | Morning HR: | Hyration: | Warm Up:
Time Of Day: | Pace: | Distance: | Weather: | Aches/Pains/Injury:
Route:

July

Week 31 ~ 7/25/2022 to 7/31/2022

Jul 25. MON

Hours Slept: | Sleep Quality: 1 2 3 4 5 | Morning HR: | Hyration: | Warm Up:
Time Of Day: | Pace: | Distance: | Weather: | Aches/Pains/Injury:
Route:

Jul 26. TUE

Hours Slept: | Sleep Quality: 1 2 3 4 5 | Morning HR: | Hyration: | Warm Up:
Time Of Day: | Pace: | Distance: | Weather: | Aches/Pains/Injury:
Route:

Jul 27. WED

Hours Slept: | Sleep Quality: 1 2 3 4 5 | Morning HR: | Hyration: | Warm Up:
Time Of Day: | Pace: | Distance: | Weather: | Aches/Pains/Injury:
Route:

Jul 28. THU

Hours Slept: | Sleep Quality: 1 2 3 4 5 | Morning HR: | Hyration: | Warm Up:
Time Of Day: | Pace: | Distance: | Weather: | Aches/Pains/Injury:
Route:

Jul 29. FRI

Hours Slept: | Sleep Quality: 1 2 3 4 5 | Morning HR: | Hyration: | Warm Up:
Time Of Day: | Pace: | Distance: | Weather: | Aches/Pains/Injury:
Route:

Jul 30. SAT

Hours Slept: | Sleep Quality: 1 2 3 4 5 | Morning HR: | Hyration: | Warm Up:
Time Of Day: | Pace: | Distance: | Weather: | Aches/Pains/Injury:
Route:

Jul 31. SUN

Hours Slept: | Sleep Quality: 1 2 3 4 5 | Morning HR: | Hyration: | Warm Up:
Time Of Day: | Pace: | Distance: | Weather: | Aches/Pains/Injury:
Route:

August

Week 32 ~ 8/1/2022 to 8/7/2022

Aug 1. MON

Hours Slept: | Sleep Quality: 1 2 3 4 5 | Morning HR: | Hyration: | Warm Up:
Time Of Day: | Pace: | Distance: | Weather: | Aches/Pains/Injury:
Route:

Aug 2. TUE

Hours Slept: | Sleep Quality: 1 2 3 4 5 | Morning HR: | Hyration: | Warm Up:
Time Of Day: | Pace: | Distance: | Weather: | Aches/Pains/Injury:
Route:

Aug 3. WED

Hours Slept: | Sleep Quality: 1 2 3 4 5 | Morning HR: | Hyration: | Warm Up:
Time Of Day: | Pace: | Distance: | Weather: | Aches/Pains/Injury:
Route:

Aug 4. THU

Hours Slept: | Sleep Quality: 1 2 3 4 5 | Morning HR: | Hyration: | Warm Up:
Time Of Day: | Pace: | Distance: | Weather: | Aches/Pains/Injury:
Route:

Aug 5. FRI

Hours Slept: | Sleep Quality: 1 2 3 4 5 | Morning HR: | Hyration: | Warm Up:
Time Of Day: | Pace: | Distance: | Weather: | Aches/Pains/Injury:
Route:

Aug 6. SAT

Hours Slept: | Sleep Quality: 1 2 3 4 5 | Morning HR: | Hyration: | Warm Up:
Time Of Day: | Pace: | Distance: | Weather: | Aches/Pains/Injury:
Route:

Aug 7. SUN

Hours Slept: | Sleep Quality: 1 2 3 4 5 | Morning HR: | Hyration: | Warm Up:
Time Of Day: | Pace: | Distance: | Weather: | Aches/Pains/Injury:
Route:

August

Week 33 ~ 8/8/2022 to 8/14/2022

Aug 8. MON

Hours Slept: | Sleep Quality: 1 2 3 4 5 | Morning HR: | Hyration: | Warm Up:

Time Of Day: | Pace: | Distance: | Weather: | Aches/Pains/Injury:

Route:

Aug 9. TUE

Hours Slept: | Sleep Quality: 1 2 3 4 5 | Morning HR: | Hyration: | Warm Up:

Time Of Day: | Pace: | Distance: | Weather: | Aches/Pains/Injury:

Route:

Aug 10. WED

Hours Slept: | Sleep Quality: 1 2 3 4 5 | Morning HR: | Hyration: | Warm Up:

Time Of Day: | Pace: | Distance: | Weather: | Aches/Pains/Injury:

Route:

Aug 11. THU

Hours Slept: | Sleep Quality: 1 2 3 4 5 | Morning HR: | Hyration: | Warm Up:

Time Of Day: | Pace: | Distance: | Weather: | Aches/Pains/Injury:

Route:

Aug 12. FRI

Hours Slept: | Sleep Quality: 1 2 3 4 5 | Morning HR: | Hyration: | Warm Up:

Time Of Day: | Pace: | Distance: | Weather: | Aches/Pains/Injury:

Route:

Aug 13. SAT

Hours Slept: | Sleep Quality: 1 2 3 4 5 | Morning HR: | Hyration: | Warm Up:

Time Of Day: | Pace: | Distance: | Weather: | Aches/Pains/Injury:

Route:

Aug 14. SUN

Hours Slept: | Sleep Quality: 1 2 3 4 5 | Morning HR: | Hyration: | Warm Up:

Time Of Day: | Pace: | Distance: | Weather: | Aches/Pains/Injury:

Route:

August

Week 34 ~ 8/15/2022 to 8/21/2022

Aug 15. MON

Hours Slept: | Sleep Quality: 1 2 3 4 5 | Morning HR: | Hyration: | Warm Up:
Time Of Day: | Pace: | Distance: | Weather: | Aches/Pains/Injury:
Route:

Aug 16. TUE

Hours Slept: | Sleep Quality: 1 2 3 4 5 | Morning HR: | Hyration: | Warm Up:
Time Of Day: | Pace: | Distance: | Weather: | Aches/Pains/Injury:
Route:

Aug 17. WED

Hours Slept: | Sleep Quality: 1 2 3 4 5 | Morning HR: | Hyration: | Warm Up:
Time Of Day: | Pace: | Distance: | Weather: | Aches/Pains/Injury:
Route:

Aug 18. THU

Hours Slept: | Sleep Quality: 1 2 3 4 5 | Morning HR: | Hyration: | Warm Up:
Time Of Day: | Pace: | Distance: | Weather: | Aches/Pains/Injury:
Route:

Aug 19. FRI

Hours Slept: | Sleep Quality: 1 2 3 4 5 | Morning HR: | Hyration: | Warm Up:
Time Of Day: | Pace: | Distance: | Weather: | Aches/Pains/Injury:
Route:

Aug 20. SAT

Hours Slept: | Sleep Quality: 1 2 3 4 5 | Morning HR: | Hyration: | Warm Up:
Time Of Day: | Pace: | Distance: | Weather: | Aches/Pains/Injury:
Route:

Aug 21. SUN

Hours Slept: | Sleep Quality: 1 2 3 4 5 | Morning HR: | Hyration: | Warm Up:
Time Of Day: | Pace: | Distance: | Weather: | Aches/Pains/Injury:
Route:

August

Week 35 ~ 8/22/2022 to 8/28/2022

Aug 22. MON

Hours Slept: Sleep Quality: 1 2 3 4 5 Morning HR: Hyration: Warm Up:

Time Of Day: Pace: Distance: Weather: Aches/Pains/Injury:

Route:

Aug 23. TUE

Hours Slept: Sleep Quality: 1 2 3 4 5 Morning HR: Hyration: Warm Up:

Time Of Day: Pace: Distance: Weather: Aches/Pains/Injury:

Route:

Aug 24. WED

Hours Slept: Sleep Quality: 1 2 3 4 5 Morning HR: Hyration: Warm Up:

Time Of Day: Pace: Distance: Weather: Aches/Pains/Injury:

Route:

Aug 25. THU

Hours Slept: Sleep Quality: 1 2 3 4 5 Morning HR: Hyration: Warm Up:

Time Of Day: Pace: Distance: Weather: Aches/Pains/Injury:

Route:

Aug 26. FRI

Hours Slept: Sleep Quality: 1 2 3 4 5 Morning HR: Hyration: Warm Up:

Time Of Day: Pace: Distance: Weather: Aches/Pains/Injury:

Route:

Aug 27. SAT

Hours Slept: Sleep Quality: 1 2 3 4 5 Morning HR: Hyration: Warm Up:

Time Of Day: Pace: Distance: Weather: Aches/Pains/Injury:

Route:

Aug 28. SUN

Hours Slept: Sleep Quality: 1 2 3 4 5 Morning HR: Hyration: Warm Up:

Time Of Day: Pace: Distance: Weather: Aches/Pains/Injury:

Route:

August

Week 36 ~ 8/29/2022 to 9/4/2022

Aug 29. MON	Hours Slept:	Sleep Quality: 1 2 3 4 5	Morning HR:	Hyration:	Warm Up:
	Time Of Day:	Pace:	Distance:	Weather:	Aches/Pains/Injury:
	Route:				
Aug 30. TUE	Hours Slept:	Sleep Quality: 1 2 3 4 5	Morning HR:	Hyration:	Warm Up:
	Time Of Day:	Pace:	Distance:	Weather:	Aches/Pains/Injury:
	Route:				
Aug 31. WED	Hours Slept:	Sleep Quality: 1 2 3 4 5	Morning HR:	Hyration:	Warm Up:
	Time Of Day:	Pace:	Distance:	Weather:	Aches/Pains/Injury:
	Route:				
Sep 1. THU	Hours Slept:	Sleep Quality: 1 2 3 4 5	Morning HR:	Hyration:	Warm Up:
	Time Of Day:	Pace:	Distance:	Weather:	Aches/Pains/Injury:
	Route:				
Sep 2. FRI	Hours Slept:	Sleep Quality: 1 2 3 4 5	Morning HR:	Hyration:	Warm Up:
	Time Of Day:	Pace:	Distance:	Weather:	Aches/Pains/Injury:
	Route:				
Sep 3. SAT	Hours Slept:	Sleep Quality: 1 2 3 4 5	Morning HR:	Hyration:	Warm Up:
	Time Of Day:	Pace:	Distance:	Weather:	Aches/Pains/Injury:
	Route:				
Sep 4. SUN	Hours Slept:	Sleep Quality: 1 2 3 4 5	Morning HR:	Hyration:	Warm Up:
	Time Of Day:	Pace:	Distance:	Weather:	Aches/Pains/Injury:
	Route:				

September

Week 37 ~ 9/5/2022 to 9/11/2022

Sep 5. MON

Hours Slept: | Sleep Quality: 1 2 3 4 5 | Morning HR: | Hyration: | Warm Up:
Time Of Day: | Pace: | Distance: | Weather: | Aches/Pains/Injury:
Route:

Sep 6. TUE

Hours Slept: | Sleep Quality: 1 2 3 4 5 | Morning HR: | Hyration: | Warm Up:
Time Of Day: | Pace: | Distance: | Weather: | Aches/Pains/Injury:
Route:

Sep 7. WED

Hours Slept: | Sleep Quality: 1 2 3 4 5 | Morning HR: | Hyration: | Warm Up:
Time Of Day: | Pace: | Distance: | Weather: | Aches/Pains/Injury:
Route:

Sep 8. THU

Hours Slept: | Sleep Quality: 1 2 3 4 5 | Morning HR: | Hyration: | Warm Up:
Time Of Day: | Pace: | Distance: | Weather: | Aches/Pains/Injury:
Route:

Sep 9. FRI

Hours Slept: | Sleep Quality: 1 2 3 4 5 | Morning HR: | Hyration: | Warm Up:
Time Of Day: | Pace: | Distance: | Weather: | Aches/Pains/Injury:
Route:

Sep 10. SAT

Hours Slept: | Sleep Quality: 1 2 3 4 5 | Morning HR: | Hyration: | Warm Up:
Time Of Day: | Pace: | Distance: | Weather: | Aches/Pains/Injury:
Route:

Sep 11. SUN

Hours Slept: | Sleep Quality: 1 2 3 4 5 | Morning HR: | Hyration: | Warm Up:
Time Of Day: | Pace: | Distance: | Weather: | Aches/Pains/Injury:
Route:

September

Week 38 ~ 9/12/2022 to 9/18/2022

Sep 12. MON

Hours Slept: | Sleep Quality: 1 2 3 4 5 | Morning HR: | Hyration: | Warm Up:
Time Of Day: | Pace: | Distance: | Weather: | Aches/Pains/Injury:
Route:

Sep 13. TUE

Hours Slept: | Sleep Quality: 1 2 3 4 5 | Morning HR: | Hyration: | Warm Up:
Time Of Day: | Pace: | Distance: | Weather: | Aches/Pains/Injury:
Route:

Sep 14. WED

Hours Slept: | Sleep Quality: 1 2 3 4 5 | Morning HR: | Hyration: | Warm Up:
Time Of Day: | Pace: | Distance: | Weather: | Aches/Pains/Injury:
Route:

Sep 15. THU

Hours Slept: | Sleep Quality: 1 2 3 4 5 | Morning HR: | Hyration: | Warm Up:
Time Of Day: | Pace: | Distance: | Weather: | Aches/Pains/Injury:
Route:

Sep 16. FRI

Hours Slept: | Sleep Quality: 1 2 3 4 5 | Morning HR: | Hyration: | Warm Up:
Time Of Day: | Pace: | Distance: | Weather: | Aches/Pains/Injury:
Route:

Sep 17. SAT

Hours Slept: | Sleep Quality: 1 2 3 4 5 | Morning HR: | Hyration: | Warm Up:
Time Of Day: | Pace: | Distance: | Weather: | Aches/Pains/Injury:
Route:

Sep 18. SUN

Hours Slept: | Sleep Quality: 1 2 3 4 5 | Morning HR: | Hyration: | Warm Up:
Time Of Day: | Pace: | Distance: | Weather: | Aches/Pains/Injury:
Route:

September

Week 39 ~ 9/19/2022 to 9/25/2022

Sep 19. MON

Hours Slept: | Sleep Quality: 1 2 3 4 5 | Morning HR: | Hyration: | Warm Up:
Time Of Day: | Pace: | Distance: | Weather: | Aches/Pains/Injury:
Route:

Sep 20. TUE

Hours Slept: | Sleep Quality: 1 2 3 4 5 | Morning HR: | Hyration: | Warm Up:
Time Of Day: | Pace: | Distance: | Weather: | Aches/Pains/Injury:
Route:

Sep 21. WED

Hours Slept: | Sleep Quality: 1 2 3 4 5 | Morning HR: | Hyration: | Warm Up:
Time Of Day: | Pace: | Distance: | Weather: | Aches/Pains/Injury:
Route:

Sep 22. THU

Hours Slept: | Sleep Quality: 1 2 3 4 5 | Morning HR: | Hyration: | Warm Up:
Time Of Day: | Pace: | Distance: | Weather: | Aches/Pains/Injury:
Route:

Sep 23. FRI

Hours Slept: | Sleep Quality: 1 2 3 4 5 | Morning HR: | Hyration: | Warm Up:
Time Of Day: | Pace: | Distance: | Weather: | Aches/Pains/Injury:
Route:

Sep 24. SAT

Hours Slept: | Sleep Quality: 1 2 3 4 5 | Morning HR: | Hyration: | Warm Up:
Time Of Day: | Pace: | Distance: | Weather: | Aches/Pains/Injury:
Route:

Sep 25. SUN

Hours Slept: | Sleep Quality: 1 2 3 4 5 | Morning HR: | Hyration: | Warm Up:
Time Of Day: | Pace: | Distance: | Weather: | Aches/Pains/Injury:
Route:

September

Week 40 ~ 9/26/2022 to 10/2/2022

Sep 26. MON	Hours Slept: Time Of Day: Route:	Sleep Quality: 1 2 3 4 5 Pace:	Morning HR: Distance:	Hyration: Weather:	Warm Up: Aches/Pains/Injury:
Sep 27. TUE	Hours Slept: Time Of Day: Route:	Sleep Quality: 1 2 3 4 5 Pace:	Morning HR: Distance:	Hyration: Weather:	Warm Up: Aches/Pains/Injury:
Sep 28. WED	Hours Slept: Time Of Day: Route:	Sleep Quality: 1 2 3 4 5 Pace:	Morning HR: Distance:	Hyration: Weather:	Warm Up: Aches/Pains/Injury:
Sep 29. THU	Hours Slept: Time Of Day: Route:	Sleep Quality: 1 2 3 4 5 Pace:	Morning HR: Distance:	Hyration: Weather:	Warm Up: Aches/Pains/Injury:
Sep 30. FRI	Hours Slept: Time Of Day: Route:	Sleep Quality: 1 2 3 4 5 Pace:	Morning HR: Distance:	Hyration: Weather:	Warm Up: Aches/Pains/Injury:
Oct 1. SAT	Hours Slept: Time Of Day: Route:	Sleep Quality: 1 2 3 4 5 Pace:	Morning HR: Distance:	Hyration: Weather:	Warm Up: Aches/Pains/Injury:
Oct 2. SUN	Hours Slept: Time Of Day: Route:	Sleep Quality: 1 2 3 4 5 Pace:	Morning HR: Distance:	Hyration: Weather:	Warm Up: Aches/Pains/Injury:

October

Week 41 ~ 10/3/2022 to 10/9/2022

Oct 3. MON

Hours Slept: | Sleep Quality: 1 2 3 4 5 | Morning HR: | Hyration: | Warm Up:
Time Of Day: | Pace: | Distance: | Weather: | Aches/Pains/Injury:
Route:

Oct 4. TUE

Hours Slept: | Sleep Quality: 1 2 3 4 5 | Morning HR: | Hyration: | Warm Up:
Time Of Day: | Pace: | Distance: | Weather: | Aches/Pains/Injury:
Route:

Oct 5. WED

Hours Slept: | Sleep Quality: 1 2 3 4 5 | Morning HR: | Hyration: | Warm Up:
Time Of Day: | Pace: | Distance: | Weather: | Aches/Pains/Injury:
Route:

Oct 6. THU

Hours Slept: | Sleep Quality: 1 2 3 4 5 | Morning HR: | Hyration: | Warm Up:
Time Of Day: | Pace: | Distance: | Weather: | Aches/Pains/Injury:
Route:

Oct 7. FRI

Hours Slept: | Sleep Quality: 1 2 3 4 5 | Morning HR: | Hyration: | Warm Up:
Time Of Day: | Pace: | Distance: | Weather: | Aches/Pains/Injury:
Route:

Oct 8. SAT

Hours Slept: | Sleep Quality: 1 2 3 4 5 | Morning HR: | Hyration: | Warm Up:
Time Of Day: | Pace: | Distance: | Weather: | Aches/Pains/Injury:
Route:

Oct 9. SUN

Hours Slept: | Sleep Quality: 1 2 3 4 5 | Morning HR: | Hyration: | Warm Up:
Time Of Day: | Pace: | Distance: | Weather: | Aches/Pains/Injury:
Route:

October

Week 42 ~ 10/10/2022 to 10/16/2022

Oct 10. MON

Hours Slept: | Sleep Quality: 1 2 3 4 5 | Morning HR: | Hyration: | Warm Up:
Time Of Day: | Pace: | Distance: | Weather: | Aches/Pains/Injury:
Route:

Oct 11. TUE

Hours Slept: | Sleep Quality: 1 2 3 4 5 | Morning HR: | Hyration: | Warm Up:
Time Of Day: | Pace: | Distance: | Weather: | Aches/Pains/Injury:
Route:

Oct 12. WED

Hours Slept: | Sleep Quality: 1 2 3 4 5 | Morning HR: | Hyration: | Warm Up:
Time Of Day: | Pace: | Distance: | Weather: | Aches/Pains/Injury:
Route:

Oct 13. THU

Hours Slept: | Sleep Quality: 1 2 3 4 5 | Morning HR: | Hyration: | Warm Up:
Time Of Day: | Pace: | Distance: | Weather: | Aches/Pains/Injury:
Route:

Oct 14. FRI

Hours Slept: | Sleep Quality: 1 2 3 4 5 | Morning HR: | Hyration: | Warm Up:
Time Of Day: | Pace: | Distance: | Weather: | Aches/Pains/Injury:
Route:

Oct 15. SAT

Hours Slept: | Sleep Quality: 1 2 3 4 5 | Morning HR: | Hyration: | Warm Up:
Time Of Day: | Pace: | Distance: | Weather: | Aches/Pains/Injury:
Route:

Oct 16. SUN

Hours Slept: | Sleep Quality: 1 2 3 4 5 | Morning HR: | Hyration: | Warm Up:
Time Of Day: | Pace: | Distance: | Weather: | Aches/Pains/Injury:
Route:

October

Week 43 ~ 10/17/2022 to 10/23/2022

Oct 17. MON

Hours Slept: | Sleep Quality: 1 2 3 4 5 | Morning HR: | Hyration: | Warm Up:
Time Of Day: | Pace: | Distance: | Weather: | Aches/Pains/Injury:
Route:

Oct 18. TUE

Hours Slept: | Sleep Quality: 1 2 3 4 5 | Morning HR: | Hyration: | Warm Up:
Time Of Day: | Pace: | Distance: | Weather: | Aches/Pains/Injury:
Route:

Oct 19. WED

Hours Slept: | Sleep Quality: 1 2 3 4 5 | Morning HR: | Hyration: | Warm Up:
Time Of Day: | Pace: | Distance: | Weather: | Aches/Pains/Injury:
Route:

Oct 20. THU

Hours Slept: | Sleep Quality: 1 2 3 4 5 | Morning HR: | Hyration: | Warm Up:
Time Of Day: | Pace: | Distance: | Weather: | Aches/Pains/Injury:
Route:

Oct 21. FRI

Hours Slept: | Sleep Quality: 1 2 3 4 5 | Morning HR: | Hyration: | Warm Up:
Time Of Day: | Pace: | Distance: | Weather: | Aches/Pains/Injury:
Route:

Oct 22. SAT

Hours Slept: | Sleep Quality: 1 2 3 4 5 | Morning HR: | Hyration: | Warm Up:
Time Of Day: | Pace: | Distance: | Weather: | Aches/Pains/Injury:
Route:

Oct 23. SUN

Hours Slept: | Sleep Quality: 1 2 3 4 5 | Morning HR: | Hyration: | Warm Up:
Time Of Day: | Pace: | Distance: | Weather: | Aches/Pains/Injury:
Route:

October

Week 44 ~ 10/24/2022 to 10/30/2022

Oct 24. MON

Hours Slept: | Sleep Quality: 1 2 3 4 5 | Morning HR: | Hyration: | Warm Up:

Time Of Day: | Pace: | Distance: | Weather: | Aches/Pains/Injury:

Route:

Oct 25. TUE

Hours Slept: | Sleep Quality: 1 2 3 4 5 | Morning HR: | Hyration: | Warm Up:

Time Of Day: | Pace: | Distance: | Weather: | Aches/Pains/Injury:

Route:

Oct 26. WED

Hours Slept: | Sleep Quality: 1 2 3 4 5 | Morning HR: | Hyration: | Warm Up:

Time Of Day: | Pace: | Distance: | Weather: | Aches/Pains/Injury:

Route:

Oct 27. THU

Hours Slept: | Sleep Quality: 1 2 3 4 5 | Morning HR: | Hyration: | Warm Up:

Time Of Day: | Pace: | Distance: | Weather: | Aches/Pains/Injury:

Route:

Oct 28. FRI

Hours Slept: | Sleep Quality: 1 2 3 4 5 | Morning HR: | Hyration: | Warm Up:

Time Of Day: | Pace: | Distance: | Weather: | Aches/Pains/Injury:

Route:

Oct 29. SAT

Hours Slept: | Sleep Quality: 1 2 3 4 5 | Morning HR: | Hyration: | Warm Up:

Time Of Day: | Pace: | Distance: | Weather: | Aches/Pains/Injury:

Route:

Oct 30. SUN

Hours Slept: | Sleep Quality: 1 2 3 4 5 | Morning HR: | Hyration: | Warm Up:

Time Of Day: | Pace: | Distance: | Weather: | Aches/Pains/Injury:

Route:

October

Week 45 ~ 10/31/2022 to 11/6/2022

Oct 31. MON

Hours Slept: | Sleep Quality: 1 2 3 4 5 | Morning HR: | Hyration: | Warm Up:
Time Of Day: | Pace: | Distance: | Weather: | Aches/Pains/Injury:
Route:

Nov 1. TUE

Hours Slept: | Sleep Quality: 1 2 3 4 5 | Morning HR: | Hyration: | Warm Up:
Time Of Day: | Pace: | Distance: | Weather: | Aches/Pains/Injury:
Route:

Nov 2. WED

Hours Slept: | Sleep Quality: 1 2 3 4 5 | Morning HR: | Hyration: | Warm Up:
Time Of Day: | Pace: | Distance: | Weather: | Aches/Pains/Injury:
Route:

Nov 3. THU

Hours Slept: | Sleep Quality: 1 2 3 4 5 | Morning HR: | Hyration: | Warm Up:
Time Of Day: | Pace: | Distance: | Weather: | Aches/Pains/Injury:
Route:

Nov 4. FRI

Hours Slept: | Sleep Quality: 1 2 3 4 5 | Morning HR: | Hyration: | Warm Up:
Time Of Day: | Pace: | Distance: | Weather: | Aches/Pains/Injury:
Route:

Nov 5. SAT

Hours Slept: | Sleep Quality: 1 2 3 4 5 | Morning HR: | Hyration: | Warm Up:
Time Of Day: | Pace: | Distance: | Weather: | Aches/Pains/Injury:
Route:

Nov 6. SUN

Hours Slept: | Sleep Quality: 1 2 3 4 5 | Morning HR: | Hyration: | Warm Up:
Time Of Day: | Pace: | Distance: | Weather: | Aches/Pains/Injury:
Route:

November

Week 46 ~ 11/7/2022 to 11/13/2022

Nov 7. MON	Hours Slept:	Sleep Quality: 1 2 3 4 5	Morning HR:	Hyration:	Warm Up:
	Time Of Day:	Pace:	Distance:	Weather:	Aches/Pains/Injury:
	Route:				
Nov 8. TUE	Hours Slept:	Sleep Quality: 1 2 3 4 5	Morning HR:	Hyration:	Warm Up:
	Time Of Day:	Pace:	Distance:	Weather:	Aches/Pains/Injury:
	Route:				
Nov 9. WED	Hours Slept:	Sleep Quality: 1 2 3 4 5	Morning HR:	Hyration:	Warm Up:
	Time Of Day:	Pace:	Distance:	Weather:	Aches/Pains/Injury:
	Route:				
Nov 10. THU	Hours Slept:	Sleep Quality: 1 2 3 4 5	Morning HR:	Hyration:	Warm Up:
	Time Of Day:	Pace:	Distance:	Weather:	Aches/Pains/Injury:
	Route:				
Nov 11. FRI	Hours Slept:	Sleep Quality: 1 2 3 4 5	Morning HR:	Hyration:	Warm Up:
	Time Of Day:	Pace:	Distance:	Weather:	Aches/Pains/Injury:
	Route:				
Nov 12. SAT	Hours Slept:	Sleep Quality: 1 2 3 4 5	Morning HR:	Hyration:	Warm Up:
	Time Of Day:	Pace:	Distance:	Weather:	Aches/Pains/Injury:
	Route:				
Nov 13. SUN	Hours Slept:	Sleep Quality: 1 2 3 4 5	Morning HR:	Hyration:	Warm Up:
	Time Of Day:	Pace:	Distance:	Weather:	Aches/Pains/Injury:
	Route:				

November

Week 47 ~ 11/14/2022 to 11/20/2022

Nov 14. MON

Hours Slept: | Sleep Quality: 1 2 3 4 5 | Morning HR: | Hyration: | Warm Up:

Time Of Day: | Pace: | Distance: | Weather: | Aches/Pains/Injury:

Route:

Nov 15. TUE

Hours Slept: | Sleep Quality: 1 2 3 4 5 | Morning HR: | Hyration: | Warm Up:

Time Of Day: | Pace: | Distance: | Weather: | Aches/Pains/Injury:

Route:

Nov 16. WED

Hours Slept: | Sleep Quality: 1 2 3 4 5 | Morning HR: | Hyration: | Warm Up:

Time Of Day: | Pace: | Distance: | Weather: | Aches/Pains/Injury:

Route:

Nov 17. THU

Hours Slept: | Sleep Quality: 1 2 3 4 5 | Morning HR: | Hyration: | Warm Up:

Time Of Day: | Pace: | Distance: | Weather: | Aches/Pains/Injury:

Route:

Nov 18. FRI

Hours Slept: | Sleep Quality: 1 2 3 4 5 | Morning HR: | Hyration: | Warm Up:

Time Of Day: | Pace: | Distance: | Weather: | Aches/Pains/Injury:

Route:

Nov 19. SAT

Hours Slept: | Sleep Quality: 1 2 3 4 5 | Morning HR: | Hyration: | Warm Up:

Time Of Day: | Pace: | Distance: | Weather: | Aches/Pains/Injury:

Route:

Nov 20. SUN

Hours Slept: | Sleep Quality: 1 2 3 4 5 | Morning HR: | Hyration: | Warm Up:

Time Of Day: | Pace: | Distance: | Weather: | Aches/Pains/Injury:

Route:

November

Week 48 ~ 11/21/2022 to 11/27/2022

Nov 21. MON

Hours Slept: Sleep Quality: 1 2 3 4 5 Morning HR: Hyration: Warm Up:

Time Of Day: Pace: Distance: Weather: Aches/Pains/Injury:

Route:

Nov 22. TUE

Hours Slept: Sleep Quality: 1 2 3 4 5 Morning HR: Hyration: Warm Up:

Time Of Day: Pace: Distance: Weather: Aches/Pains/Injury:

Route:

Nov 23. WED

Hours Slept: Sleep Quality: 1 2 3 4 5 Morning HR: Hyration: Warm Up:

Time Of Day: Pace: Distance: Weather: Aches/Pains/Injury:

Route:

Nov 24. THU

Hours Slept: Sleep Quality: 1 2 3 4 5 Morning HR: Hyration: Warm Up:

Time Of Day: Pace: Distance: Weather: Aches/Pains/Injury:

Route:

Nov 25. FRI

Hours Slept: Sleep Quality: 1 2 3 4 5 Morning HR: Hyration: Warm Up:

Time Of Day: Pace: Distance: Weather: Aches/Pains/Injury:

Route:

Nov 26. SAT

Hours Slept: Sleep Quality: 1 2 3 4 5 Morning HR: Hyration: Warm Up:

Time Of Day: Pace: Distance: Weather: Aches/Pains/Injury:

Route:

Nov 27. SUN

Hours Slept: Sleep Quality: 1 2 3 4 5 Morning HR: Hyration: Warm Up:

Time Of Day: Pace: Distance: Weather: Aches/Pains/Injury:

Route:

November

Week 49 ~ 11/28/2022 to 12/4/2022

Nov 28. MON

Hours Slept: Sleep Quality: 1 2 3 4 5 Morning HR: Hyration: Warm Up:
Time Of Day: Pace: Distance: Weather: Aches/Pains/Injury:
Route:

Nov 29. TUE

Hours Slept: Sleep Quality: 1 2 3 4 5 Morning HR: Hyration: Warm Up:
Time Of Day: Pace: Distance: Weather: Aches/Pains/Injury:
Route:

Nov 30. WED

Hours Slept: Sleep Quality: 1 2 3 4 5 Morning HR: Hyration: Warm Up:
Time Of Day: Pace: Distance: Weather: Aches/Pains/Injury:
Route:

Dec 1. THU

Hours Slept: Sleep Quality: 1 2 3 4 5 Morning HR: Hyration: Warm Up:
Time Of Day: Pace: Distance: Weather: Aches/Pains/Injury:
Route:

Dec 2. FRI

Hours Slept: Sleep Quality: 1 2 3 4 5 Morning HR: Hyration: Warm Up:
Time Of Day: Pace: Distance: Weather: Aches/Pains/Injury:
Route:

Dec 3. SAT

Hours Slept: Sleep Quality: 1 2 3 4 5 Morning HR: Hyration: Warm Up:
Time Of Day: Pace: Distance: Weather: Aches/Pains/Injury:
Route:

Dec 4. SUN

Hours Slept: Sleep Quality: 1 2 3 4 5 Morning HR: Hyration: Warm Up:
Time Of Day: Pace: Distance: Weather: Aches/Pains/Injury:
Route:

December

Week 50 ~ 12/5/2022 to 12/11/2022

Dec 5. MON

Hours Slept: Sleep Quality: 1 2 3 4 5 Morning HR: Hyration: Warm Up:

Time Of Day: Pace: Distance: Weather: Aches/Pains/Injury:

Route:

Dec 6. TUE

Hours Slept: Sleep Quality: 1 2 3 4 5 Morning HR: Hyration: Warm Up:

Time Of Day: Pace: Distance: Weather: Aches/Pains/Injury:

Route:

Dec 7. WED

Hours Slept: Sleep Quality: 1 2 3 4 5 Morning HR: Hyration: Warm Up:

Time Of Day: Pace: Distance: Weather: Aches/Pains/Injury:

Route:

Dec 8. THU

Hours Slept: Sleep Quality: 1 2 3 4 5 Morning HR: Hyration: Warm Up:

Time Of Day: Pace: Distance: Weather: Aches/Pains/Injury:

Route:

Dec 9. FRI

Hours Slept: Sleep Quality: 1 2 3 4 5 Morning HR: Hyration: Warm Up:

Time Of Day: Pace: Distance: Weather: Aches/Pains/Injury:

Route:

Dec 10. SAT

Hours Slept: Sleep Quality: 1 2 3 4 5 Morning HR: Hyration: Warm Up:

Time Of Day: Pace: Distance: Weather: Aches/Pains/Injury:

Route:

Dec 11. SUN

Hours Slept: Sleep Quality: 1 2 3 4 5 Morning HR: Hyration: Warm Up:

Time Of Day: Pace: Distance: Weather: Aches/Pains/Injury:

Route:

December

Week 51 ~ 12/12/2022 to 12/18/2022

Dec 12. MON

Hours Slept: | Sleep Quality: 1 2 3 4 5 | Morning HR: | Hyration: | Warm Up:
Time Of Day: | Pace: | Distance: | Weather: | Aches/Pains/Injury:
Route:

Dec 13. TUE

Hours Slept: | Sleep Quality: 1 2 3 4 5 | Morning HR: | Hyration: | Warm Up:
Time Of Day: | Pace: | Distance: | Weather: | Aches/Pains/Injury:
Route:

Dec 14. WED

Hours Slept: | Sleep Quality: 1 2 3 4 5 | Morning HR: | Hyration: | Warm Up:
Time Of Day: | Pace: | Distance: | Weather: | Aches/Pains/Injury:
Route:

Dec 15. THU

Hours Slept: | Sleep Quality: 1 2 3 4 5 | Morning HR: | Hyration: | Warm Up:
Time Of Day: | Pace: | Distance: | Weather: | Aches/Pains/Injury:
Route:

Dec 16. FRI

Hours Slept: | Sleep Quality: 1 2 3 4 5 | Morning HR: | Hyration: | Warm Up:
Time Of Day: | Pace: | Distance: | Weather: | Aches/Pains/Injury:
Route:

Dec 17. SAT

Hours Slept: | Sleep Quality: 1 2 3 4 5 | Morning HR: | Hyration: | Warm Up:
Time Of Day: | Pace: | Distance: | Weather: | Aches/Pains/Injury:
Route:

Dec 18. SUN

Hours Slept: | Sleep Quality: 1 2 3 4 5 | Morning HR: | Hyration: | Warm Up:
Time Of Day: | Pace: | Distance: | Weather: | Aches/Pains/Injury:
Route:

December

Week 52 ~ 12/19/2022 to 12/25/2022

Dec 19. MON

Hours Slept: | Sleep Quality: 1 2 3 4 5 | Morning HR: | Hyration: | Warm Up:
Time Of Day: | Pace: | Distance: | Weather: | Aches/Pains/Injury:
Route:

Dec 20. TUE

Hours Slept: | Sleep Quality: 1 2 3 4 5 | Morning HR: | Hyration: | Warm Up:
Time Of Day: | Pace: | Distance: | Weather: | Aches/Pains/Injury:
Route:

Dec 21. WED

Hours Slept: | Sleep Quality: 1 2 3 4 5 | Morning HR: | Hyration: | Warm Up:
Time Of Day: | Pace: | Distance: | Weather: | Aches/Pains/Injury:
Route:

Dec 22. THU

Hours Slept: | Sleep Quality: 1 2 3 4 5 | Morning HR: | Hyration: | Warm Up:
Time Of Day: | Pace: | Distance: | Weather: | Aches/Pains/Injury:
Route:

Dec 23. FRI

Hours Slept: | Sleep Quality: 1 2 3 4 5 | Morning HR: | Hyration: | Warm Up:
Time Of Day: | Pace: | Distance: | Weather: | Aches/Pains/Injury:
Route:

Dec 24. SAT

Hours Slept: | Sleep Quality: 1 2 3 4 5 | Morning HR: | Hyration: | Warm Up:
Time Of Day: | Pace: | Distance: | Weather: | Aches/Pains/Injury:
Route:

Dec 25. SUN

Hours Slept: | Sleep Quality: 1 2 3 4 5 | Morning HR: | Hyration: | Warm Up:
Time Of Day: | Pace: | Distance: | Weather: | Aches/Pains/Injury:
Route:

December

Week 53 ~ 12/26/2022 to 1/1/2023

Dec 26. MON

Hours Slept: | Sleep Quality: 1 2 3 4 5 | Morning HR: | Hyration: | Warm Up:

Time Of Day: | Pace: | Distance: | Weather: | Aches/Pains/Injury:

Route:

Dec 27. TUE

Hours Slept: | Sleep Quality: 1 2 3 4 5 | Morning HR: | Hyration: | Warm Up:

Time Of Day: | Pace: | Distance: | Weather: | Aches/Pains/Injury:

Route:

Dec 28. WED

Hours Slept: | Sleep Quality: 1 2 3 4 5 | Morning HR: | Hyration: | Warm Up:

Time Of Day: | Pace: | Distance: | Weather: | Aches/Pains/Injury:

Route:

Dec 29. THU

Hours Slept: | Sleep Quality: 1 2 3 4 5 | Morning HR: | Hyration: | Warm Up:

Time Of Day: | Pace: | Distance: | Weather: | Aches/Pains/Injury:

Route:

Dec 30. FRI

Hours Slept: | Sleep Quality: 1 2 3 4 5 | Morning HR: | Hyration: | Warm Up:

Time Of Day: | Pace: | Distance: | Weather: | Aches/Pains/Injury:

Route:

Dec 31. SAT

Hours Slept: | Sleep Quality: 1 2 3 4 5 | Morning HR: | Hyration: | Warm Up:

Time Of Day: | Pace: | Distance: | Weather: | Aches/Pains/Injury:

Route:

Jan 1. SUN

Hours Slept: | Sleep Quality: 1 2 3 4 5 | Morning HR: | Hyration: | Warm Up:

Time Of Day: | Pace: | Distance: | Weather: | Aches/Pains/Injury:

Route:

Running Goals

Goal:

Plan/Strategy:

Start Date: Deadline:

Goal:

Plan/Strategy:

Start Date: Deadline:

Goal:

Plan/Strategy:

Start Date: Deadline:

Goal:

Plan/Strategy:

Start Date: Deadline:

Running Goals

Goal:

Plan/Strategy:

Start Date: Deadline:

Goal:

Plan/Strategy:

Start Date: Deadline:

Goal:

Plan/Strategy:

Start Date: Deadline:

Goal:

Plan/Strategy:

Start Date: Deadline:

Running Goals

Goal:

Plan/Strategy:

Start Date: Deadline:

Goal:

Plan/Strategy:

Start Date: Deadline:

Goal:

Plan/Strategy:

Start Date: Deadline:

Goal:

Plan/Strategy:

Start Date: Deadline:

Running Goals

Goal:

Plan/Strategy:

Start Date: Deadline:

Goal:

Plan/Strategy:

Start Date: Deadline:

Goal:

Plan/Strategy:

Start Date: Deadline:

Goal:

Plan/Strategy:

Start Date: Deadline:

Running Goals

Goal:

Plan/Strategy:

Start Date: Deadline:

Goal:

Plan/Strategy:

Start Date: Deadline:

Goal:

Plan/Strategy:

Start Date: Deadline:

Goal:

Plan/Strategy:

Start Date: Deadline:

Running Goals

Goal:

Plan/Strategy:

Start Date: Deadline:

Goal:

Plan/Strategy:

Start Date: Deadline:

Goal:

Plan/Strategy:

Start Date: Deadline:

Goal:

Plan/Strategy:

Start Date: Deadline:

Running Goals

Goal:

Plan/Strategy:

Start Date: Deadline:

Goal:

Plan/Strategy:

Start Date: Deadline:

Goal:

Plan/Strategy:

Start Date: Deadline:

Goal:

Plan/Strategy:

Start Date: Deadline:

Running Goals

Goal:

Plan/Strategy:

Start Date: Deadline:

Goal:

Plan/Strategy:

Start Date: Deadline:

Goal:

Plan/Strategy:

Start Date: Deadline:

Goal:

Plan/Strategy:

Start Date: Deadline:

My Races

Date	Event/Location	Distance	Time/Place	Notes/Reflections

My Races

Date	Event/Location	Distance	Time/Place	Notes/Reflections

My Races

Date	Event/Location	Distance	Time/Place	Notes/Reflections

My Races

Date	Event/Location	Distance	Time/Place	Notes/Reflections

My Races

Date	Event/Location	Distance	Time/Place	Notes/Reflections

My Races

Date	Event/Location	Distance	Time/Place	Notes/Reflections

My Races

Date	Event/Location	Distance	Time/Place	Notes/Reflections

My Races

Date	Event/Location	Distance	Time/Place	Notes/Reflections

My Races

Date	Event/Location	Distance	Time/Place	Notes/Reflections

Yearly Running Tracker

		1	2	3	4	5	6	7	8	9	10	11	12	13	14	15
JAN	P															
	D															
FEB	P															
	D															
MAR	P															
	D															
APR	P															
	D															
MAY	P															
	D															
JUN	P															
	D															
JUL	P															
	D															
AUG	P															
	D															
SEP	P															
	D															
OCT	P															
	D															
NOV	P															
	D															
DEC	P															
	D															

Total Miles For The Year:

16	17	18	19	20	21	22	23	24	25	26	27	28	29	30	31	Total Miles

Designed By:
ZENRUNNINGLOG